THE ANTHRACITE IRON INDUSTRY OF THE LEHIGH VALLEY

by

Craig L. Bartholomew

and

Lance E. Metz

edited by

Ann Bartholomew

D1496317

Center for Canal History and Technology

1988

Published in cooperation with

The Society for Industrial Archaeology

Copyright © 1988 by Center for Canal History and Technology

Published by
Center for Canal History and Technology
Hugh Moore Historical Park and Museums, Inc.
P.O. Box 877, Easton, Pa. 18044-0877

Printed by
Harmony Press
Phillipsburg, N.J.

Library of Congress Cataloguing in Publication Data

Bartholomew, Craig L., 1938-
    The anthracite iron industry of the Lehigh Valley / by Craig L.
Bartholomew and Lance E. Metz ; edited by Ann Bartholomew.
        p.   cm.
    "Published in cooperation with the Society for Industrial
Archaeology."
    Bibliography: p.
    ISBN 0-930973-08-9 (pbk.)
    1. Iron industry and trade--Pennsylvania--Lehigh River
Valley--History.   2. Iron foundries--Pennsylvania--Lehigh River
Valley--History.   I. Metz, Lance E., 1947-   . II. Bartholomew, Ann
M. III. Title.
HB9547.P4B35 1988
338.4'76691'0974--dc19   88-25719
                                                          CIP

TABLE OF CONTENTS

INTRODUCTION

History does not repeat itself in detail, but there are remarkable similarities between the Severn River Valley in the 18th century and the Lehigh Valley in the 19th century. Both Valleys are called "Birthplace of the Industrial Revolution." The one, the birthplace of the British Industrial Revolution, the other, birthplace of the American Industrial Revolution. Both valleys were the world's center of iron production. One in the second half of the 18th Century, the other in the late 19th Century.

The above quotation from the 1980 NOVA P.B.S. Television production, "The Bridge that Spanned the World," is a concise statement of the importance of the Lehigh Valley to the chronicle of the development of America's iron industry. This region of eastern Pennsylvania was the first place in America where the iron industry was transformed from a rural plantation-based system into a modern large scale enterprise. It was in the Lehigh Valley that anthracite coal was first used to fuel a commercially successful blast furnace and it was here that many of the technological and managerial innovations were developed that created the modern American military industrial complex.

This book is the first attempt to relate the story of the Lehigh Valley's iron industry in a comprehensive manner. It is the end product of the efforts of many individuals. Without the historical knowledge of the authors and the archival resources of the Hugh Moore Historical Park and Museums, and the Lehigh County Historical Society it could not have been compiled. Without the cooperation of scholars such as James Lee and Brian Morrell, the stories of many furnaces could not have been related. Most importantly, it was the editing and many hours of devoted labor by Ann Bartholomew that gave this work its final form.

David Thomas as he appeared in 1845. He was an experienced, middle-aged ironmaster when he came to the Lehigh Valley in 1839. He later became known as the father of the modern American Iron Industry. *Courtesy Lehigh County Historical Society.*

CHAPTER I

CANAL, COAL AND IRON

In February 1874 David Thomas traveled from his home in Catasauqua to attend an Iron Masters Convention in Philadelphia where, at the start of the proceedings, he was elected the convention's president. Then in his eightieth year, the unassuming Welshman had spent 62 of those years in the iron trade, first in his native Glamorganshire and since 1839 in the Lehigh Valley. The honor bestowed on Thomas at the convention was not his first: only two years earlier, he had been selected as the first president of the newly formed American Institute of Mining Engineers.

Shortly after Thomas's death on June 20, 1882, James Swank, secretary and general manager of the American Iron and Steel Association, paid him this tribute:

David Thomas's character and services to the American iron trade are held in high honor by all American iron and steel manufacturers. He is affectionately styled the Father of the American Anthracite-Iron Industry, because the furnace built under his direction at Catasauqua, and blown in by him, was the first of all the early anthracite furnaces that was completely successful, both from an engineering and a commercial standpoint; and also because he subsequently became identified with the manufacture of anthracite pig iron on a more extensive scale than any of his contemporaries.

The anthracite iron industry with which "Father" Thomas was so closely identified was born on the banks of the Lehigh River in eastern Pennsylvania. The development of this industry made the Lehigh Valley, perhaps more than any other single region, the "Birthplace of the Industrial Revolution in America." Anthracite technology made possible the production of cheap iron, the essential ingredient of industrialization: iron for rails and boiler plate that built railroads; iron for plows that broke the prairie sod; iron for the farm machinery that harvested burgeoning yields. Near the end of the nineteenth century, Lehigh Valley iron, converted into steel, would be forged into armor plate and guns for the warships that won the Spanish American War and for Teddy Roosevelt's Great White Fleet, the ships that displayed the United States' naval power in their famous 1907 voyage around the world. Later it would be rolled into the wide-flanged beams that made possible New York City's skyscrapers.

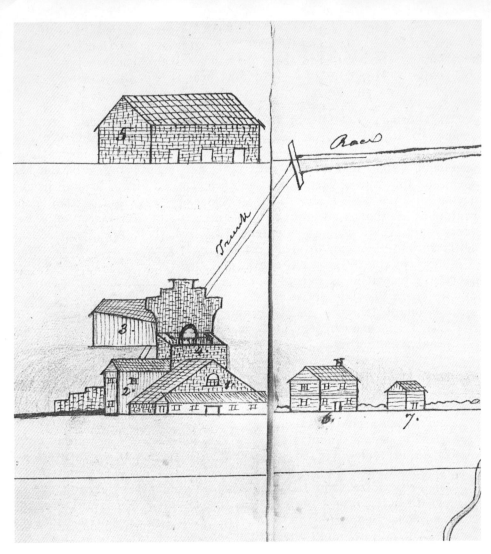

Layout of the Lehigh Furnace, Lehigh County, dated 1828. The operators submitted this sketch to their insurance company, along with a plea for reduced rates: "There is far more danger in a Jersey Furnace than there is in a Penn'a. A Jersey Furnace is apt to blow (that is burst and of course burn up without any chance or hope of extinguishing the same) which is not the case with the Penn'a Furnaces . . . our regulations are different from other Furnaces every person must remain on his post day and night, which is not the case with other Furnaces in this part of the country, which is an additional safeguard, and our casting house is also built of stone which I believe is not the case in any other Furnace in the country - and so is the coal house built of stone, we think that $20 would be a reasonable sum."
1. Casting house, built of stone; 2. Bellows and water house, built of wood; 3. Bridge House, built of wood; 4. Stack, 30 feet at the foundation and 32 feet high, built of stone, with a guard wall which protects the bridge house; 5. Coal House, built of stone; 6. Warehouse, built of logs; 7. Spring-house, built of logs.
Courtesy Lehigh County Historical Society.

That the Lehigh Valley should have this distinction seems almost fortuitous, for it was not a center of early iron production as was neighboring Schuylkill Valley. Only one blast furnace operated in the Lehigh Valley during the colonial era; it was located at Durham on the Valley's southern fringe. During the early nineteenth century only three additional charcoal furnaces were built—the Hampton Furnace, constructed in 1809 at Sigmunds, was nestled in the wooded hills of southwest Lehigh County; Lehigh Furnace was built in 1826 at the base of the huge timber reserves of the Kittatinny Ridge to the north; the Catherine Furnace was built around the same time near Nazareth, at Jacobsburg in Henry's Woods. This furnace, surrounded by farmland, survived only a decade or so before the local timber reserves were depleted. The Hampton (later Sigmunds) and Lehigh furnaces survived into the third quarter of the century because of their proximity to more abundant sources of charcoal.

These furnaces, however, were an anomaly in the Lehigh Valley. Before the fourth decade of the nineteenth century, the Valley's economy was predominantly agricultural and the manner of life nearly completely rural. Well-kept farms of moderate size with sturdy stone homes and barns filled the landscape. Generations of industrious Pennsylvania German farmers had cleared the land and their descendants continued to till the rich limestone and shale soils of the Valley with care and diligence. The few small towns and villages that existed served as market centers for the farmers of the surrounding countryside, places where surplus crops could be sold or exchanged for those items that could not be produced on the farm.

Allentown and Easton, because of their status as county seats, were the only towns of any consequence; still in 1840 Allentown had a population of only 2,493 persons. The Moravian villages of Bethlehem and Emmaus had only recently opened their communities to people of other faiths. The few small and scattered industries were directly related to needs of an agricultural society -- grist, linseed, cloverseed, and fulling mills, small foundries and forges for plows and other farm implements, blacksmith shops, wagon and carriage makers, saw mills, and planing mills. While the basic ingredients for the establishment of a local iron industry were available in the Lehigh Valley, the first settlers were men of the soil, farmers who were unfamiliar with the methods of iron production. Rather than convert the vast forests into charcoal, they cut its trees to clear the land for agriculture and to build their homes and barns. The waste products, the stumps, branches, and bark, were burned to ashes for potash for household use and to fertilize their fields. The abundant limestone was not quarried for furnace flux but burned to quicklime for use in mortar and to condition the soil. If their plows happened to turn over a lump of iron ore, great quantities of which lay just beneath the soil's surface, it went unrecognized or ignored. The social and economic hegemony of agriculture was unchallenged until the fourth decade of the nineteenth century.

The Schuylkill Valley, on the other hand, was a major center for iron production, both in the colonial period and well into the nineteenth century. Indeed, the first furnace in Pennsylvania was built in 1720 along the Manatawny Creek, a tributary of the Schuylkill, at Colebrookdale, just west of Boyertown in Berks County. The South Mountains, rich in magnetic ores and timber for charcoal, soon saw their forests cut and their hillsides stripped to fuel the scores of furnaces that followed.

At the beginning of the nineteenth century, the heart of iron-making activities began to shift to the heavily forested ridges and valleys of central Pennsylvania. Whereas proximity to ore and to waterpower had been the most significant factors in establishing the locations of the earliest iron furnaces, by the nineteenth century the availability of timber became the single most important consideration. Then, as now, iron production was an energy-intensive activity. Even a well-managed charcoal furnace had a voracious appetite for fuel -- a typical early-nineteenth-century charcoal furnace, capable of producing an average of 600 tons per year, consumed the charcoal equivalent of at least one acre of timber a day. Assuming an average blast of 300 days per year and a 30-year reforestation cycle, a timber reserve of 9,000 acres was required to assure continual operation. Some furnace owners were both far-sighted and wealthy enough to acquire such reserves; as a result, charcoal iron production continued through the late nineteenth century. However, most charcoal furnaces shut down when they had exhausted the available supplies of reasonably priced charcoal.

The expense of conveying iron to seaboard markets from increasingly remote furnace sites, or of bringing charcoal to the older, established furnaces, precluded the production of large quantities of inexpensive iron. Thus, at a time when the demand for iron was increasing, charcoal iron was becoming more and more costly.

The same problem had confronted British ironmakers a century earlier, when Britain's forests had become nearly depleted after centuries of shipbuilding and charcoal production. In England the problem was solved in 1709 when Abraham Darby successfully used coked coal in his furnace at Coalbrookdale in Shropshire. Through trial and error in selecting coal and coking methods, he eventually produced a coke that was capable of making good quality iron. Darby's historic furnace is preserved today as part of the Iron Bridge museum complex.

Josiah White (1780-1850) and his partner Erskine Hazard (1790-1865) co-founded the Lehigh Coal and Navigation Company and played catalytic roles in making the Lehigh Valley a birthplace of the American Industrial Revolution. *From Matthew Henry, History of the Lehigh Valley, Easton, PA, 1860.*

By the mid-eighteenth century, ironmasters throughout the British Isles were following Darby's lead and were operating their furnaces with coke. As a blast fuel, coke has a number of advantages over charcoal and raw coal. To the British ironmakers, its most important advantage was simply its availability. Bituminous coal of suitable coking quality was abundant throughout the Midlands and in northern England, South Wales, and central Scotland. It produced a fuel that was very high in fixed carbon, which enhanced its reductant ability, and very low in sulphur and ash.

Coke has a cellular structure which many believed was the reason for its capacity to support rapid combustion. A second significant characteristic is its strength. Both raw bituminous coal and charcoal are relatively weak and friable and are not well suited to withstanding the heavy load of the burden in a large furnace. If either of these fuels is crushed, the production rate of the furnace is greatly retarded because of the restriction of the blast through the burden. However, carefully blended coals that have been subjected to good coking practices will produce a coke capable of supporting the weight of the iron ore and limestone, without crumbling, in even the tallest furnace stack. Coke's freedom from volatile matter and bitumen, which are driven off in the coking process, make it very stable and clean-burning under high temperatures.

While anthracite coal is stronger than coke at ambient temperatures, and is therefore shipped more easily and economically than coke, it contains three to four percent volatile matter. When nineteenth century ironmakers first tried using anthracite, they found that even this small percentage of volatile matter contributed to the decrepitation of the coal, which sometimes occurred when anthracite was subjected to blast-furnace temperatures, creating one of the problems often experienced when raw bituminous coal or charcoal were used in larger furnaces. Probably the most important advantage of coke over anthracite is its weight; it is only half as dense. Ton for ton, it occupies nearly twice as much volume as anthracite in the furnace stack, therefore its wider distribution through the burden allowed a furnace fueled with coke to be driven far more rapidly than one fueled with anthracite. For all these reasons, coke has become the fuel of choice for modern ironmakers.

While Darby's invention greatly stimulated iron production in Britain, it did not have the same effect in the United States. Good quality coking coals were not discovered in this country until the 1840s and were not seriously exploited until the late 1860s. The American charcoal-iron producer of the early nineteenth century soon discovered he had difficulty competing in the open market with the cheaper British coke iron, which was being imported in increasingly greater quantities. This did not mean that charcoal iron production ceased, but that it represented an increasingly smaller proportion of the iron marketed in America. As mineral fuels came to be used for ironmaking, charcoal iron was reserved for a few applications requiring its greater purity and tensile strength, such as chilled railroad car wheels. The eventual relegation of costly charcoal iron to specialized uses and the unavailability of good coking coals forced Americans to turn to the mineral fuel that had been discovered in the rugged hills and valleys of northeastern Pennsylvania: anthracite coal.

By the second half of the eighteenth century, some coal was being used for domestic heating, and even for some ironmaking activities, in the seaboard cities of the English colonies. It arrived by ship either from the James River area near Richmond, Virginia, or was imported from England. This coal was the bituminous variety that could easily be burned on open grates. While some anthracite coal was used in a few blacksmith forges and to heat some homes in the remote anthracite region of Pennsylvania the second half of the eighteenth century, it was not until during the War of 1812, when

James River and English coal became virtually unobtainable, that much attention was paid to this "stone coal."

ANTHRACITE

The first Philadelphian of record to use anthracite for working iron was Joshua Malin, who as early as 1803 used anthracite mixed with a substance described as coke to heat wrought iron in Samuel Mifflin's Philadelphia slitting mill. Not much came of this experiment until 1812 when Malin, then a partner with Armor Bishop in a Delaware County ironworks, purchased a load of Schuylkill anthracite from Colonel George Shoemaker of Pottsville. Malin apparently had some success in using this coal; when Shoemaker later increased the price, he opened a pit of his own, also near Pottsville. In 1813, Malin purchased a half interest in the Valley Forge on the Schuylkill River, where he claimed to have successfully used anthracite to remelt pig iron in an air furnace. The 1827 volume of the Journal of the Franklin Institute contains a description of an anthracite blast furnace devised by Joshua Malin of Lebanon, Pennsylvania, but no mention is made of its success.

The load of coal purchased by Malin was one of nine that Colonel Shoemaker had shipped to the Philadelphia area in 1812. Most of those who tried using his coal "declared Shoemaker an impostor, for attempting to impose stone on them for coal, and were clamorous against him. Not discouraged by the sneers and sarcasms cast upon him, he persisted in the undertaking, and at last succeeded in disposing of two loads, for the cost of transportation . . . and the remaining seven he gave to persons who promised to try to use it, and lost all the coal and charges." The other load that Shoemaker was able to sell was purchased by Josiah White and Erskine Hazard for their wire mill at the Falls of the Schuylkill.

White and Hazard also had difficulty in getting anthracite to burn. In his "History of the Introduction of Anthracite Coal in Philadelphia," Erskine Hazard wrote: "a whole night [was] spent in endeavoring to make a fire in the furnace when the hands shut the furnace door and left the mill in despair. Fortunately, one of them left his jacket in the mill, and, returning for it in about half an hour, noticed that the door was red hot, and upon opening it was surprised to find the whole furnace of a glowing white heat. The others were summoned, and four separate parcels of iron were heated and rolled by the same fire before it required renewing. The furnace was then replenished, and, as letting it alone had succeeded so well, it was concluded to try again, and the experiment was repeated with the same result." White and Hazard were so impressed with this discovery that they immediately encouraged the formation of a company to improve the navigation of the Schuylkill to bring greater quantities of anthracite to the Philadelphia market at a reasonable price. However, when the Schuylkill Navigation Company was chartered in 1815, White was denied election as one of its managers. Thus rebuffed, and discouraged by the high tolls set by the Schuylill Navigation Company, White turned his attention to the Lehigh River.

The eastern prong of the southern anthracite field had been discovered by Phillip Ginder in 1791 on Sharp Mountain, at the present site of the borough of Summit Hill. Since this coal was transported to market by way of Mauch Chunk and the Lehigh River Valley, it has traditionally been known as Lehigh coal. It is the hardest and purest anthracite found in Pennsylvania and the most difficult to ignite. However, once ignited, it burns very hot, with almost no flame, and leaves a powdery white ash. It was to become a prized fuel for iron production.

Ginder had shared his discovery with Colonel Jacob Weiss of Fort Allen (now Weissport), to whom he had previously sold the land on which the coal outcropped. Shortly thereafter, on February 13, 1792, Colonel Weiss and several Philadelphia friends formed the Lehigh Coal Mine Company. This company obtained from Weiss, and by subsequent warrants from others, approximately 8,000 acres at the eastern end of the Panther Valley. While some coal was mined soon afterwards, the activity shortly ceased because of the difficulty in getting the coal to market. In December 1807 a lease was granted to two men, Rowland and Butland, to try to develop the property, but they failed to mine any coal and the lease was forfeited the next year. Still hopeful of profiting from their assets, the owners granted a 10-year lease to Jacob Cist, Charles Miner, and John W. Robinson in December, 1813. Of this Wilkes-Barre group, Cist was the most vigorous proponent of anthracite. He had earlier promoted the construction of a canal between the Susquehanna and the Delaware rivers to ship Wyoming Valley anthracite to the Philadelphia market. But efforts for the new leaseholders produced little more immediate success than was achieved by their predecessors. In 1814, the group sent only five coal arks down the Lehigh; the two that eventually completed the journey were purchased by White and Hazard.

During the month of December 1817, Josiah White and George F. Hauto visited the mines at Summit Hill and inspected the course of the Lehigh River for its development potential. White concluded that a way could be found to market the Lehigh coal profitably. He also discovered that the lease of Cist and his partners had lapsed because of their inability to market a sufficient quantity of coal. Upon application, White, Hazard, and Hauto were granted a 20-year lease on the mines. They were given three years to develop the property, after which they were required to deliver at least 40,000 bushels of coal to Philadelphia annually. Rent on the property was one ear of corn per year, payable on demand.

The terms for improving the Lehigh Navigation, probably the most generous in United States history, were established by the state legislature on March 20, 1818. Originally, two separate companies were formed, the Lehigh Navigation Company and the Lehigh Coal Company. On March 7, 1820, Hazard and White bought out Hauto's interest and on April 21, 1820, the two companies were merged into the Lehigh Navigation and Coal Company. A further reorganization occurred, with an accompanying increase in stock, on May 1, 1821; the new name was the Lehigh Coal and Navigation Company. Navigation of the Lehigh, first by a combination of slackwater pools and artificial freshets, then by a combination canal-and-slackwater-pool system, became one of the most successful and enduring transportation systems in American history.

By the early 1830s, anthracite coal was being distributed in rapidly increasing quantities to the cities of the eastern seaboard. The Delaware and Hudson Canal carried northern-field anthracite to the Hudson River and thence to New York City, Albany, and New England ports. The North Branch and its connecting canals carried coal from the Wyoming Valley to Baltimore and points along the route. The Schuylkill Navigation carried southern- and middle-field coal to Philadelphia, where it was both consumed and trans-shipped to other ports. Lehigh Navigation coal penetrated both the Philadelphia and the New York markets, the first via the state-owned Delaware Canal and the second via both the Morris and the Delaware and Raritan canals. Even the Union Canal participated in the coal trade, carrying anthracite first to the homes and later to the furnaces of the Lebanon Valley via the Pine Grove feeder.

With the transportation system developed, the fuel was available for the technological ferment of the 1830s. During this decade the trials and tribulations of scores of ironmakers and entrepreneurs would eventually culminate with the successful production of iron using anthracite coal. The cheaper iron that resulted was a catalyst for the industrial revolution in America. Steam engines, machine tools, textile machinery, rails and locomotives, agricultural implements and machinery, mining equipment, and the tools of war all required great quantities of inexpensive iron.

Leaders in the scientific, business, and political communities were well aware of the importance of successfully smelting iron with mineral fuel. Beginning in 1825, the Franklin Institute offered a gold medal to anyone who was successful in smelting ore and producing at least 20 tons of iron using mineral fuel. Nicholas Biddle, president of the Bank of the United States, and some of his business associates offered a $5,000 prize to the first person keeping a furnace in blast using anthracite alone for at least 90 days. In 1835, the state provided for a geological survey primarily to learn more about Pennsylvania's coal and iron deposits. Also in 1835, Hazard's Register of Pennsylvania suggested that the Pennsylvania legislature award premiums for producing pig iron with anthracite coal. On June 16, 1836, a bill sponsored by Charles B. Penrose of Cumberland, Perry County, was enacted to encourage the manufacture of iron with coke or mineral coal by authorizing the governor to form a joint stock company for that purpose. The pages of the Journal of the Franklin Institute were filled with accounts of experiments with mineral fuels. The Journal published patents, and within its pages dialogues were carried on for months and even years on theories and practices for using anthracite in blast furnaces. Articles from Europe's leading scientific journals describing similar experiments in Britain and the continent were also reprinted and commented upon.

Skilled ironworkers and mechanics from England, Scotland, and Wales had been emigrating to the United States in increasing numbers, bringing with them their experience and knowledge of the most modern British practices. These men contributed significantly to the technological advancements made in the iron industry, both by taking charge of furnace plants and by passing on their knowledge to native ironmakers.

By 1840, the process was complete. Anthracite iron was being produced successfully on a commercial basis in a handful of small furnaces in eastern Pennsylvania. During the next decade, dozens more anthracite furnaces were constructed in Pennsylvania and even a few in the adjoining states of New Jersey and New York. By 1855, more iron was produced in a few score large anthracite furnaces located along the improved navigation systems than was made in the hundreds of smaller charcoal stacks scattered throughout the nation's rural districts. Both transportation economies and the lower price of coal contributed to the lower price of anthracite iron.

EARLY EXPERIMENTS

There are three major nineteenth century accounts of the trials and experiments that led to the commercially successful production of anthracite iron. The most contemporary, and in most respects the most detailed, was written by Walter R. Johnson, who was affiliated with the Franklin Institute, the University of Pennsylvania, and nearly every other scientific and technical organization in existence at that time. His book, entitled Notes on the Use of Anthracite in the Manufacture of Iron, With Some Remarks on Its Evaporating Power, was published in Boston in 1841. The first half is devoted to descriptions of the anthracite furnaces built to that date as well as to a very detailed report of the important experimental work that had been performed in 1827 by Messieurs Gueymard and Robin at Vizille on the border of France and Switzerland.

The second work, "Sketch of Early Anthracite Furnaces," published in Volume III of the Transactions of the American Institute of Mining Engineers, was written by William Firmstone, the builder and longtime superintendent of the Glendon Iron Works. His work is based loosely on Johnson's earlier book, to whom he acknowledged his debt and to which he added his own observations. Of the three writers, Firmstone alone was an active ironmaster during the development of anthracite technology and he is typical of the skilled British immigrants who contributed so much to the industry. In 1839, he was employed by Henry C. Carey, John White, and Burd Paterson to operate a furnace at Karthaus on the West Branch of the Susquehanna River. Firmstone employed a hot blast and ran the furnace on coke, but the venture was soon discontinued because of poor ore. Before building the Glendon Works, he also blew in the furnace at Phoenixville with anthracite as its fuel. He died at his residence near Easton on September 11, 1877.

The third publication is James M. Swank's masterpiece, The Manufacture of Iron in All Ages. Swank drew upon his experience and the resources of his position as Secretary of the American Iron and Steel Association to provide an overview of all iron and steel production to the end of the nineteenth century. Writing at the time when anthracite ironmaking was declining in importance, he was able to comment on the significance of the anthracite era in the industrial development of the United States.

Walter F. Johnson began his study with a description of the trials of Gueymard and Robin at Vizille. In their well- financed effort they experienced, and documented, all the problems associated with trying to use anthracite with a cold blast. Johnson noted that "in making the experiments at Vizille, every appliance then at the command of the iron manufacturer appears to have been brought to bear upon the success of the undertaking." The furnace was constructed to the highest standards of the day. "It was 40 feet 4 inches across the boshes, with a chimney 14 feet above the latter; and the pitch of the boshes was 57°. An engine of 80 horsepower was employed to furnish blast, the pressure of which was sometimes urged as high as 4 lbs. to the square inch." The hearth, boshes, and inwalls were lined with the best firebrick and the furnace was equipped with three tuyeres which could be used either singly or all at once.

In late 1827, the furnace was blown in using only coke as fuel and excellent foundry iron was obtained. "The first experiment with

WILLIAM FIRMSTONE

In 1835 William Firmstone emigrated from the ironmaking region of the Severn Valley in Shropshire, England, to the United States. After serving as an itinerant ironmaster at various furnaces in Ohio and Pennsylvania, he began the development of the Glendon Iron Company in 1842. A technically innovative engineer and a competent businessman, he served as superintendent at Glendon until his death in 1877. *From Sixty Seventh Anniversary of the Founding of Glendon, Easton, PA, 1909.*

14

anthracite was made by substituting for one tenth of the coke an equal weight of anthracite. The effect of this change was to render the metal, if anything, rather better than before, and only to retard slightly the descent of the charges." As more anthracite was added, in increments of one tenth the weight of coke, the descent of the burden was increasingly retarded and the quality of the iron steadily deteriorated. At one-half anthracite, "A new retardation was at once perceived: cinder was thrown out not only at the tympe, but even at the tuyeres." The experiment was then discontinued due to an accident in which one of their workmen was crushed to death at the bottom of one of the blowing cylinders.

After repairing the machinery, the furnace was blown in again on January 19, 1828. The previous results were again reproduced until reaching one-half anthracite. Then "the anthracite burst and fell in fine pieces, which choked the furnace and impeded the blast. In this state of things the expedient was adopted of charging the furnace with raw instead of roasted mine, which had the effect of keeping the burthen from cohering, allowed freedom to the blast, and obviated the projection of cinders from the tympe and tuyeres." As the percentage of anthracite was increased by increments of one tenth to a total of nine tenths, the quality of iron further deteriorated and operating problems greatly increased. "As the committee of proprietors in Paris wished to have the experiments pushed to the utmost, M. Gueymard finally ordered the furnace to be charged with anthracite alone. From the moment this was done, the tuyeres became and continued black; the cinder was surcharged with iron, no casting could be obtained; the metal half refined into malleable iron, stuck fast in the hearth." After coke was again charged, the furnace resumed operating. On this experiment, Walter R. Johnson commented that "whatever can be expected from anthracite of the kind there used, when burned by means of cold blast, was probably realized in the experiments at Vizille." Others in Britain and the United States experienced nearly identical results. Among those individuals who failed were White and Hazard in their small experimental furnace at Mauch Chunk and George Crane and David Thomas at Yniscedwyn, Wales, throughout the 1820s and early 1830s.

USE OF HOT BLAST

At the time Johnson compiled his history, the world had already learned that iron could be produced with anthracite only if the blast were preheated. Until 1820, the idea of using heated blast in their furnaces does not appear to have occurred to any ironmasters. In fact, the prevailing opinion was that colder air was of higher quality than warmer air, this opinion being the result of long observations that furnaces worked better in the winter than in the summer. Without any further investigation, the ironmasters attributed this fact to the temperature of the atmosphere alone, giving no thought to the moisture of the air and to other considerations.

It was a gasworks manager, James Beaumont Neilson, not an ironmaster, who developed the concept of the hot blast. Neilson, the son of a millwright who for a time had been employed at Scotland's Carron Iron Works, was born in Shettleston, a village near Glasgow, in 1792. After an apprenticeship as an engineer, he secured employment as a foreman at the Glasgow Gas Works in 1817. He soon introduced many improvements in the manufacture of coal gas and eventually became manager of the works. Around 1825, Neilson was approached by the manager of the Muirkirk Iron Works about a blast furnace located a half mile from the blowing engine that did not make as much iron as two furnaces that were close to the same engine.

Neilson postulated that since air expands when heated, perhaps if the air were passed through a red-hot chamber before entering the furnace, its volume would be increased and the more distant furnace would do the same work as the other two. He experimented first by feeding heated air to a gas light and then to a blacksmith's fire. In both cases improvements were noted. Neilson then decided to try the same plan on a larger scale in a blast furnace. Early in 1829, he was given the chance to implement his ideas at the Clyde Iron Works in Glasgow. "The apparatus consisted of a small wrought iron chamber about 4 feet long, 3 feet high and 2 feet wide set in brickwork with a grate below, similar in all respects to the ordinary steam boiler." A separate chamber was built for each tuyere and the air from the blowing engine was passed through these chambers before entering the tuyeres.

The initial results were encouraging enough that Neilson took out a patent entitled "Hot Blast for Furnaces," dated February 18, 1829. Subsequently, improvements were made to the heating apparatus, until its final form closely resembled the iron pipe stove ultimately used by Crane and Thomas at Yniscedwyn. The hot blast not only improved production in coke-fueled furnaces, but enabled Scottish ironmakers to use raw coal and the local black band ironstone in their furnaces. As very few Scottish coals produced good metallurgical coke, this proved a real boon to the Scottish iron trade. By 1835, the hot blast was in general use in Britain; Neilson, after years of court battles, was able to retire in 1847 on the royalties from his patent.

A few years after the introduction of Neilson's hot blast, Dr. Frederick W. Geissenhainer, a Lutheran clergyman from New York City, applied the hot-blast concept to making iron with anthracite coal. Geissenhainer, who had earlier spent some years in eastern

Pennsylvania, owned a small charcoal furnace near Pottsville, Schuylkill County. He also operated a small experimental furnace near his home in New York where he claimed to have successfully smelted iron ore with anthracite coal and a "heated air blast." On September 5, 1831, he filed for a patent on his process; the patent was granted on December 19, 1833. In order to prove out his theory on a practical scale, Geissenhainer constructed the Valley Furnace along the Silver Creek in Schuylkill County during 1836. He operated this furnace only two months, in August and September of 1836, before his machinery broke down. Only small quantities of iron were produced. He became ill before he was able to rebuild and try again, and died on May 27, 1838. It is very likely that Geissenhainer was aware of Neilson's patent, for in his own application he stated "Though I cannot and do not claim an exclusive right of the use of heated air for any kind of fuel, nevertheless, I do believe to have a right to claim and do claim the use of heated air, applied upon and in connexion with the said principle and manner discovered by me, to smelt iron in blast furnaces, with anthracite coal." He further stressed that the blast had to be in such quantity, velocity and density, or under such pressure, as the compactness and the continuity of the anthracite coal requires.

While Geissenhainer was conducting his trials near Pottsville, George Crane, owner of the Yniscedwyn Iron Works near Swansea in South Wales, and his superintendent, David Thomas, were thinking along the same lines. In his application for a British patent, sealed on September 28, 1836, and enrolled March 28, 1837, George Crane stated that "the object of my invention, is the application of such anthracite or stone coal, combined with hot air blast, in the smelting or manufacture of iron from iron-stone, mine or ore." As had Geissenhainer before him, Crane noted: "I do not claim the using of a hot-air blast separately, in the smelting and manufacturing of iron . . . But what I do claim as my invention is the application of anthracite or stone coal and culm, combined with the using of hot air blast in the smelting and manufacture of iron."

Crane and Thomas proved out their theory on February 7, 1837, when they successfully produced good quality iron at the rate of 34 to 36 tons per week using anthracite alone as fuel.

In September, 1837, in an address before the Chemical Section of the British Association for the Advancement of Science at Liverpool, George Crane recollected how he came upon the idea of using a heated blast on anthracite: "One evening after I had placed a piece of it upon my parlour fire (which had before been made up with Bituminous coal) and had allowed it to arrive at a red heat, upon my applying as fierce a blast to this piece of coal as I could raise from a pair of bellows, I noticed the appearance of a black mark or spot upon that part of it where the air impinged upon it; on my continuing the like rapid current, in the same direction, I shortly blew the fire out of it . . . On giving the thing but a moment's reflection, the question occurred to me, What would be the effect of turning a blast into a furnace upon this coal, which would itself burn--which would itself melt lead?"

David Thomas recalled that evening somewhat differently. In a commemorative article written by Ed Roberts for the April and May editions of The Cambrian, Roberts recalls "an interesting anecdote in connection with his [David Thomas's] hearing of Mr. Neilson's invention. It appears he was one evening at the house of Mr. George Crane, a gentleman who then owned the Yniscedwyn Works, and who always burnt anthracite coal in the grate of his sitting room. Mr. Thomas began to blow the fire with a small pair of bellows. 'Don't do that David, or you will blow the fire out,' interposed Mr. Crane. 'If the air out of that bellows were only as hot as Mr. Neilson describes his hot blast to be,' rejoined Mr. Thomas, 'the anthracite coal in that grate would burn like pine wood.' Mr. Crane exclaimed, 'Ah! That is the idea precisely,' and this idea both recognized as one which would bear working out; and through Mr. Thomas' indomitable pluck and perseverance it succeeded."

Soon after the idea had occurred to Crane, or to Crane and Thomas at the same time, Thomas was dispatched to Scotland to see James Neilson's invention firsthand. After the most careful examination he determined that the new hot blast was just what was wanted for an anthracite furnace. He returned to Yniscedwyn with a license from Mr. Neilson, and an expert mechanic who understood the construction of the heating ovens.

While Crane's patent was published in the Journal of the Franklin Institute in 1838, thereby making his invention public knowledge among American ironmakers, it is certain that the managers of the Lehigh Coal & Navigation Company had received the news much earlier. Josiah White's nephew, Solomon W. Roberts, was touring Welsh iron-works at that time, inspecting rails for the newly formed Philadelphia & Reading Railroad. Roberts was at the Dowlais Iron Works when he heard the news. He then "visited Mr. Crane's establishment in May, 1837, for the purpose of seeing the process and of satisfying himself that the materials used were similar to those which exist so abundantly in Pennsylvania." Roberts went on to say: "Finding that the great object was accomplished, and that the results were highly gratifying, he communicated the fact to his friends in Philadelphia, by whom it was shortly after made public through the newspapers."

The news from Wales stimulated renewed efforts by White and Hazard. The experimental furnace constructed in 1826, in which they had experienced failure similar to that of Gueymard and Robin, was reactivated, the new experiments being conducted by the firm of Baughman, Guiteau & Company. In a letter to Walter R. Johnson dated November 9, 1840, F.C. Lowthrop, who later became a member of that firm, recalled: "During the fall and winter of the year 1837, Messrs. Joseph Baughman, Julius Guiteau and Henry High, of Reading, made their first experiment in smelting iron with anthracite coal, in an old furnace at Mauch Chunk, temporarily fitted up for the purpose; they used about eighty per cent of anthracite, and the result was such as to surprise those who witnessed it (for it was considered as an impossibility even by ironmasters); and to encourage the persons engaged in it, to go on. In order, therefore, to test the matter more thoroughly, they built a furnace on a small scale, near the Mauch Chunk Weigh Lock, which was completed during the month of July 1838."

This experimental furnace was only 21½ feet high by 22 feet square at the base; the bosh was 5½ feet across. The two blowing cylinders were wood, each 6 feet in diameter; they were powered by a 14-foot overshot water wheel. "The blast was applied August 27th, and the furnace was kept in blast until September 10th, when they were obliged to stop in consequence of the apparatus for heating the blast proving to be too temporary. Several tons of iron were produced of Nos. 2 and 3 quality. I do not recollect the proportion of anthracite used. Temperature of the blast did not exceed 200 Fahrenheit." During the autumn of 1838, an improved heating apparatus was procured. It consisted of 1½-inch-thick cast iron pipes, totaling 200 feet in length which were placed in a brick chamber at the trunnel head of the furnace where they were "heated by a flame issuing thence. The blast was again applied about the last of November, 1838, and the furnace worked remarkably well for about five weeks, exclusively with anthracite coal; we were obliged, however, for want of ore, to blow out on the 12th of January, 1839." The average blast temperature during the five week period was about 400 Fahrenheit. The following season additional modifications were made. The furnace was again blown in on July 26, 1839, and continued in operation until November 2 of that year, worked exclusively with anthracite. The temperature of the blast varied between 400 and 600 F.

While Baughman, Guiteau & Company were the first to achieve any real success with anthracite in this country, their results were not wholly satisfactory. The furnace was strictly experimental and was incapable of producing quality iron for long periods on a commercial scale. As Walter R. Johnson commented: "The iron produced was of various, but mostly inferior qualities, owing probably to a deficiency of blast. Their apparatus for hot blast was at first defective, and was afterwards placed at the trunnel head, where it could not be so well regulated as if arranged in separate ovens, with an independent fire."

DAVID THOMAS

The managers of the Lehigh Coal and Navigation Company, encouraged by, but apparently not wholly satisfied with, the experiments at Mauch Chunk, sent Erskine Hazard to Wales to negotiate with George Crane. Hazard, accompanied by his eldest son, Alexander, arrived in Wales in November, 1838. By the time of Hazard's arrival, Crane was the holder not only of the British patent for making anthracite iron, but also of the U.S. patent. Soon after receiving the British patent on his process, Crane had applied for a patent in the United States but was denied one because Dr. Geissenhainer's patent covered the same principle. Crane then purchased the doctor's patent from the executors of his estate in 1838, and in November of the same year he patented additions to it.

It is extremely doubtful that White and Hazard ever expected Crane to leave his interests in Wales. His furnaces were profitable and he expected his patents to have similiar success. Instead, it is more reasonable to assume that Hazard planned to discuss royalties and also to engage someone who could duplicate Crane's achievement in Pennsylvania. For this purpose, Crane suggested his superintendent, David Thomas. Thomas certainly had the experience and qualifications for the task as he had spent all his adult life in the iron trade and had supervised the modifications to the cupola furnace in which anthracite iron had first been made.

David Thomas was born on November 3, 1794, at Tyllwyd in the Parish of Cadoxton (about midway between Alltwen and Neath), Glamorganshire, South Wales. He attended schools in both Alltwen and Neath, leaving at the age of 17 to gain employment at the Neath Abbey Iron Works. In 1817, after a five-year apprenticeship, he entered the employ of the Yniscedwyn Iron Works, then owned by Richard Parsons, where he was appointed superintendent of both the mines and the furnaces. Almost immediately after Thomas obtained this position, Richard Parsons and his brother Samuel suffered financial difficulties and the works were taken over by a Mr. Haines, a banker from Swansea who was the mortgagee. During this period the furnaces were operated only sporadically and Thomas spent the time surveying for the Brecon Forest tramroad to Sennybridge for John Christie, and may also have helped Christie open the Drim anthracite colliery.

In 1823, the Yniscedwyn Works were sold to George Crane of Broomsgrove, Worcestershire. Crane had retired in 1820 after 15 years in the hardware business in Birmingham. In 1823 he visited

Wales where he became interested in the iron trade. During Crane's ownership of the works, Thomas was encouraged to continue his experiments with anthracite. According to Thomas, "I began, as early as 1820, to make experiments. I had some anthracite coal put in the furnace with coke, in the proportion of from one part in twenty to one part in twelve. This did very well; but whenever anything went wrong with the furnace the fault was always laid on the coal; and the men became so prejudiced against it that it was given up. Still, every year I would try some experiments both in cupolas and blast furnaces. In 1825, I had a small furnace erected, with a 9 foot bosh and 25 foot stack. After blowing it in with coke, I introduced anthracite coal, increasing the amount of it by degrees; but the tuyeres would close up, so that it was abandoned. In 1830, this furnace was enlarged, giving it a bosh 11 feet in diameter, with a 45 foot stack. This resulted in a greater amount of success; yet the whole thing was so unprofitable that it was given up." Thus Thomas's early experiments pretty much duplicated the failures of his contemporaries who had tried using anthracite with cold blast.

Prior to Erskine Hazard's visit, David Thomas had moved his family from Yniscedwyn to Devynock (now Defynnog), in order to provide a better education for his children. To commute to his work at Yniscedwyn (now spelled Ynys-Cedwyn), Thomas traveled the 18 or 20 miles over the tramroad (later the Swansea Vale Branch of the Neath & Brecon Railway, now abandoned) that he had earlier constructed. It was over this same tramroad that George Crane took Hazard to interview David Thomas at his home near Devynock Station. Hazard apparently was satisfied with Thomas's credentials, for he offered him the position in America. Thomas was at first reluctant to leave his native land, chiefly on account of his aged mother, but his wife persuaded him that the new world held larger opportunities for her three sons.

The complete text of the contract between David Thomas and the proposed Lehigh Crane Iron Company is reproduced in Samuel Thomas's Reminiscences. The "Memorandum of Agreement" consisted of four clauses. First, Thomas must agree "to remove with his family to the works to be established by the said company on or near the River Lehigh, and there to undertake the erection of a blast-furnace as furnace-manager; also to give his assistance in finding mines of iron-ore, fire-clay, and other materials suitable for carrying on iron-works, and generally give his best knowledge and services to the said company, in the prosecution of the iron-business, in such manner as will best promote their interests, for the term of five years from the time of his arrival in America, provided the experiment of smelting iron with anthracite coal should be successful there."

21

Agreement between Erskine Hazard, acting on behalf of the Lehigh Crane Iron Company, and David Thomas, for Thomas to build an anthracite-fueled blast furnace along the Lehigh Navigation. *Hugh Moore Historical Park & Museums, Inc., Easton, PA.*

Secondly, the company agreed to pay the moving expenses of Thomas and his family "from his present residence to the works . . . on the Lehigh, and there to furnish him a salary at the rate of two hundred pounds sterling a year from the time of his stipend ceasing in his present employment until the first furnace on the Lehigh is got into blast with anthracite coal and making good iron, and, after that, at the rate of two hundred and fifty pounds sterling shall be added to his annual salary." Thomas would receive an additional fifty pounds a year for each additional furnace put into blast under his management; within the first ten years of his employment, he built five furnaces for the Lehigh Iron Company.

The third clause provided for failure. It was mutually agreed "that should the said Thomas fail of putting a furnace into successful operation with anthracite coal . . . the said company shall then pay the said Thomas a sum equivalent to the expense of removing himself and his family from the Lehigh to their present residence."

The fourth clause set the exchange rate for settling Thomas's salary at four shillings and sixpence to the dollar. The agreement was signed by David Thomas and by Erskine Hazard "for Lehigh Crane Iron Comp'y" and witnessed by Alexander Hazard, on December 31, 1838.

LEHIGH CRANE IRON COMPANY

Prior to Hazard's journey to Wales, the Lehigh Crane Iron Company existed only in the minds of its promoters, principally White and Hazard. On January 10, 1839, the first meeting of its directors was held in Philadelphia, at which time Robert Earp was elected president and treasurer and John McAllister, Jr., secretary. The other directors were Josiah White, Erskine Hazard, George and Thomas Earp, and Nathan Trotter. On April 23, 1839, they entered into "Articles of Association of the Lehigh Crane Iron Co., Made and Entered into Under and Pursuant to an Act to Encourage the Manufacture of Iron with Coke, or Mineral Coal and for other purposes, Passed June 16, 1836" by the Pennsylvania Legislature. These articles of association established the name of the company, its location, either Lehigh or Northampton County, the capital stock ($100,000) and the procedures for payment of same. The articles were signed by the aforementioned directors and by Theodore Mitchell, an additional stockholder. A charter for 25 years was granted to the Lehigh Crane Iron Company on May 16, 1839, under the June 16, 1836, Act of the Legislature referred to in the Articles.

On October 2, 1838, in anticipation of the organization of the Lehigh Crane Iron Company, and to promote the development of other iron-producing and coal-consuming enterprises along their canal, the Board of Managers of the Lehigh Coal & Navigation Company adopted a resolution to provide free water rights to those building anthracite-fueled iron works. The Company would "give in fee simple all the water power of any one of the dams between Allentown and Parryville (except so much thereof as may be necessary for the navigation and one hundred inches of water under a three foot head) . . . to any company which shall raise a Capital of fifty thousand dollars thereof in improving the site for iron works and in making the experiment of manufacturing iron on the plan of George Crane of Wales." The fee for the waterpower was to become vested in the company "either upon their succeeding in keeping a furnace at work for three months in the making of iron at the rate of 27 tons a week or in case of failure when they shall show to the satisfaction of the Lehigh Company that they expended the sum of $30,000 in making the attempt. The land belonging to the Company [L.C.& N.] suitable for using said water power upon and not necessary for navigation shall also be included in the deed." The Company also stipulated that the height and location of the dam must be specified, that work must be started by July 1, 1839, and at least $15,000 be expended in the work within two years from that date. The offer was limited to the region between Allentown and Parryville because it was the most undeveloped section of the navigation; it represented a significant concession because the canal company was enjoying considerable revenues from the sale of waterpower rights downstream from Allentown, especially in the Easton area.

At their meeting of January 3, 1839, the Company's managers acknowledged receipt of a letter dated November 9, 1838, from a group consisting of Erksine Hazard, Josiah White, Robert, George and Thomas Earp, Thomas Mitchell, John McAllister, Jr., and Jonathan K. Hassinger, of whom all but the last were to become directors of the Lehigh Crane Iron Company, accepting the offer contained in the October 2 resolution. However, as neither this group, nor any other, had met the Company's conditions by the July 1, 1839, deadline, and recognizing that "it is of the utmost importance to this Company that the business of making iron with anthracite coal should be established on the Lehigh as speedily as possible," the managers of the Lehigh Coal and Navigation Company met on July 2, 1839, to rescind the first resolution and pass a second in revised form. The revised resolution made no reference to George Crane of Wales; it simply specified that the iron had to be smelted with anthracite coal. The initial capital requirement was reduced from $50,000 to $30,000. While the production rate of 27 tons per week was retained, the three month requirement was eliminated. The other revisions were minor. The deadline on this new resolution was September 1, 1839. On July 8, 1839, the directors of the Lehigh Crane Iron Company accepted the Company's offer. On December 15,

1840, the Lehigh Crane Iron Company, having met all the imposed conditions, was granted a conveyance of the property and water rights by the Lehigh Coal and Navigation Company.

THOMAS COMES TO AMERICA

During the first week of May, 1839, David Thomas and his family left Swansea on a coastal steamer for Liverpool. There they boarded the sailing packet Roscius, one of the finest ships afloat, for the voyage to New York. In his Reminiscences, Samuel Thomas recalled that after a near- record 23-day crossing:

> Our first month on American soil was spent in New Brighton, Staten Island, where my father lay very ill of a fever . . . On his recovery, he took me with him to Philadelphia, where he had been called to attend a meeting of the Crane Co.'s Board, relative to his entering upon his duties. We returned to New Brighton July 4, and two days later turned our faces toward the Lehigh Valley, our future home, taking the New Jersey railroad via Jersey City and New Brunswick, -- at that time the terminus of the road, which . . . was laid with strap-rails.
>
> From New Brunswick the journey was continued by stage, the first night being spent at Easton, and Allentown being reached on July 9. Here we resided four months while our home was being built near the new works. On July 11 my father and I started on foot for the site of the future works, near what was then known as Biery's bridge, where we spent several hours, making measurements from which to work out plans for the construction of the plant -- I, then a boy of thirteen, carrying one end of the tape-line.

Samuel Thomas, the oldest son of David Thomas, was born on March 13, 1827. Like his father, his life was dedicated to the anthracite iron industry. He was one of the leading spirits of the Lehigh Valley's iron industry until his death on February 20, 1906.

Actual construction on the first furnace for the Lehigh Crane Iron Company commenced about August 1, 1839. The construction activities, the contractors employed, and the technical specifications are discussed in detail by Samuel Thomas in his Reminiscences. The stack was 45 feet high from the base of the hearth to the trunnel head, with a chimney extending about 12 feet above the trunnel head. It was constructed of limestone, 30 feet square at the base and tapering to about 23 feet square at the top. It was lined with two courses of nine-inch-thick firebrick with a two-to-three-inch-thick clay packing between the lining and the stone to provide for the expansion of the lining. "The hot-blasts, with the usual bed-pipes, consisted of four ovens of 12 arched pipes each, 5

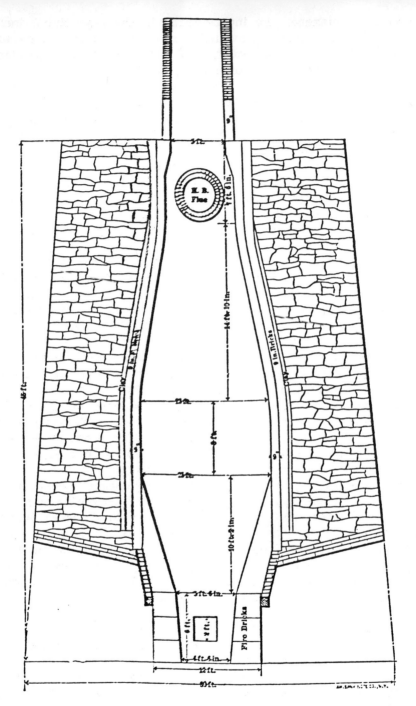

Sketch showing configuration and dimensions of No. 1 Furnace of the Lehigh Crane Iron Company. *From Transactions of the American Institute of Mining Engineers*, Vol. *XXIX, 1899.*

inches interior diameter, 1½ inches thick in the legs and 2 inches thick in the arch. They were built on the ground and fired with coal, having deep closed ash-pits, into which blast was introduced for active combustion, in lieu of a draft stack."

The blast was heated to about 600 and compressed by "a breast-wheel 12 feet in diameter and 24 feet long; the fall of 8 feet between the canal-levels at lock 36 furnishing the power. On each end of the wheel were segments on its circumference, of 10-inch face, geared into pinions on double cranks, these driving two blowing-cylinders having a 5 ft. diameter and 6 ft. stroke, with parallel motion, and worked by beams on gallows-frames. The blast from the cylinders was conducted underneath the canal through an 18-inch cast-iron pipe; this being the only receiver, the strokes of the cylinders could be counted at the furnace-tuyere as easily as in the wheel-house."

On instructions from Hazard, Thomas had ordered much of the machinery for this furnace from shops and foundries in Wales. Eventually all the equipment arrived, shipped by canal from Philadelphia, except for the blowing cylinders which were too large for the hatches on the first vessel. "At this time there was not a boring-mill in the United States large enough to bore a cylinder of 60 inches in diameter . . . Application was then made to Merrick & Towne of Southwark foundry, Philadelphia, who agreed to undertake the work, enlarging their boring mill for the purpose."

By the summer of 1840, "After many vexatious delays, the furnace was completed and successfully blown in at 5 o'clock P.M. July 3, 1840, and the first cast of about 4 tons of iron was made on the memorable 4th of July of that year, the keepers in charge of the furnace being William Phillips and Evan Jones."

The proportion of ores used was about one fourth magnetic and three fourths brown hematite (limonite). The magnetite came from the Irondale, Byram, and Dickerson mines in New Jersey and the hematite from Rice's mine, near Schoenersville, Hanover Township. "The furnace remained in blast until its fires were quenched by the rising waters of the great flood of January [7 & 8], 1841, a period of six months, during which 1080 tons of pig-iron were produced. The largest output for one week was 52 tons."

OTHER ATTEMPTS

The furnace built by David Thomas at Biery's Bridge (now Catasauqua) was not the first to make iron with anthracite coal in the United States, but it was the first to be both a technological and a commercial success. Indeed, both Firmstone and Swank completed their commentaries on the development of the anthracite iron industry with their descriptions of this furnace. William Firmstone

Artist's view of the first furnace built at Catasauqua by David Thomas in 1840.
From *Popular Science Monthly*, Vol. 38, No. 4, 1891.

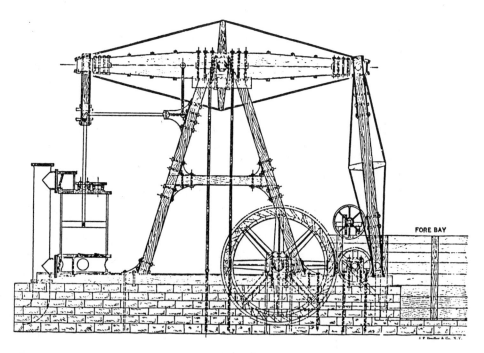

FORE BAY

Water-powered blowing engine for Furnace No. 1 at the Crane Iron Works, Catasauqua.
From *Transactions of the American Institute of Mining Engineers*, Vol. XXIX, 1899.

asserted 34 years later: "With the erection of this furnace commenced the era of high and larger furnaces and better blast machinery, with consequent improvements in yield and quality of iron
produced." More than any other single achievement to that time, it
signaled the beginning of the industrial revolution in America.

However, despite David Thomas's significant accomplishments, it
is only fair to review the experiences of those individuals who
preceded him in making anthracite iron in the United States. There
were many others who were claimants for the accolades most often,
and probably most correctly, bestowed on Thomas.

In a letter to the editor of the Coal and Iron Record, reprinted
in the Appendix of Mathews and Hungerford's History of the Counties
of Lehigh and Carbon, James Pott of Harrisburg claimed a portion of
the honor for his father, John Pott, who he said used anthracite to
smelt iron at the Manheim Iron Works at Cressona on the West Branch
of the Schuylkill as early as 1836-37. He maintained that the
anthracite was used "first in connection with charcoal, then with
wood cut short, like stove-wood, and finally, by making some change
in the interior of the furnace, with anthracite alone, a hot-blast
having already been attached." According to his son, John Pott was
convinced that he had demonstrated the practicality for using
anthracite to reduce iron ore but modifications to his works were
required before he could demonstrate it conclusively. Supposedly
the modifications were undertaken in 1840, but the whole works was
destroyed in a "terrible ice-freshet" in the spring of 1841. James
Swank made a passing notice of the effort, but neither Johnson nor
Firmstone mentioned it at all.

Another early effort, also not wholly successful, was that of
Jarvis Van Buren at South Easton. The furnace was built in 1837
and, according to an account published in the March 7, 1838, edition
of The Whig, Van Buren had produced some iron using no fuel but
anthracite. This optimistic report asserted that the iron was of the
very best quality. However, in a letter dated March 12, 1838, from
William Henry to his brother Mathew, the experienced ironmaster
noted that "the quality of the iron is much deteriorated by the use
of anthracite, in point of tenacity." It is doubtful that the poor
quality was due to the use of anthracite, since many millions of
tons of grade Ax iron were produced in anthracite-fueled furnaces
over the next 50 years. James M. Swank commented that while Van
Buren made about 20 tons of pig iron early in 1838, operations were
stopped because the blast was too weak. Swank was unsure whether
the blast was hot or cold.

Van Buren, apparently aware of the limited success of his
achievement, sought additional capital to make improvements to his
equipment. According to a legal notice appearing in the January

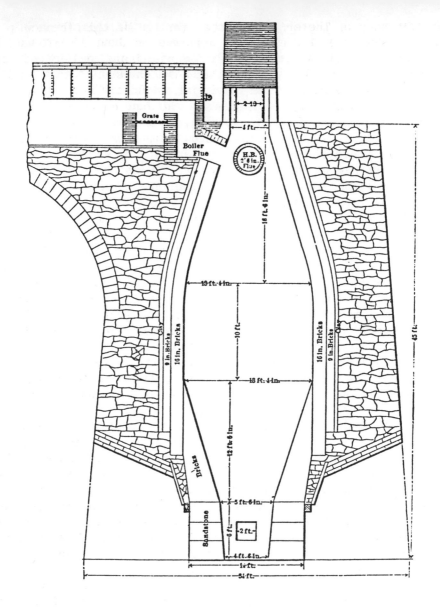

When Furnace No. 2 was built at Catasauqua in 1842, the hot blast was heated by waste gas instead of by a separate heating apparatus on the ground, as was used for No. 1 Furnace. *From Transactions of the American Institute of Mining Engineers, Vol. XXIX, 1899.*

30, 1839, copy of The Whig, he entered into a limited partnership to begin on December 15, 1838, and conclude on June 15, 1839. The partners, all Northampton County residents, included Elizabeth and Thomas McKeen, Franklin L. Crane, J.J. Ross, Christian Martin, William Ross, Michael Cavanaugh, John Drinkhouse, Robert M'Clarl, Washington M'Cartney and William Nyce. Apparently the funding provided by this partnership was insufficient to cover all of the expensive alterations Van Buren thought he needed. Attempts to obtain additional funds from the partners were unsuccessful. They had become discouraged with the prospects for success and allowed the partnership to dissolve upon its scheduled termination date of June 15, 1839. Their investment, a total of $5,250, was completely lost. For Van Buren too, the venture was a financial failure. The Easton Sentinel on Friday August 23, 1839, carried a notice that Van Buren had executed a voluntary assignment to William Nyce "of all his Household Goods, etc. for the benefit given that all persons having any claims or demands against the said assignor individually, are . . . to present them without delay." David Thomas claimed to have seen Van Buren's furnace soon after he arrived in the early summer of 1839. He commented: "It was run some ten days or two weeks, when it chilled, and proved a failure, both financially and as a furnace." Neither Johnson nor Firmstone mentioned this furnace.

The work of Baughman, Guiteau & Company at Mauch Chunk, which was described earlier, was considered significant but inconclusive by all three writers.

Probably the most important effort, prior to Thomas's at Catasauqua, was the work of Patterson, Lyman, and Perry at Pottsville. The Pottsville Furnace, sponsored by entrepreneur Burd Patterson, was built by William Lyman of Boston in 1838-39. It was 35 feet high, 30 feet square at its base and had an 8 foot, 9 inch bosh. Blast was provided by two 40-inch diameter blowing cylinders with a 6-foot stroke driven by a 15-inch steam cylinder. The power developed was estimated to be 80 horsepower. The blast, heated in ovens at the base of the furnace to about 600 F, was first applied, unsuccessfully, on July 10, 1839.

Firmstone attributed the initial failure to the lack of experience of those in charge. Johnson's commentary on some of the early experiments conducted at this furnace would seem to support Firmstone's opinion. In any case, Burd Patterson subsequently engaged Benjamin Perry, who had earlier blown in the Farrandsville Furnace on coke, to take charge of the furnace. Perry successfully applied blast on October 19, 1839. Benjamin Perry, formerly the furnace manager of the Pentyweyn Iron Works in Monmouthshire, South Wales, had emigrated to the United States in 1838 to conduct the coke and bituminous coal experiments at Farrandsville. He was

31

familiar with both Neilson's hot blast process and Crane's work at Yniscedwyn.

The Pottsville Furnace was the first to remain in blast exclusively with anthracite for a period of at least three months and therefore its builder, William Lyman, was awarded the $5,000 prize offered by Nicholas Biddle. On January 18, 1840, an award banquet was held for Lyman at the Mount Carbon House in Pottsville. It was a joyous event for the promoters of anthracite. When the dinner and speeches were over, Nicholas offered a toast to "OLD PENNSYLVANIA--her sons like her soil: rough outside, but solid stuff within; plenty of coal to warm her friends, and plenty of iron to cool her enemies."

While Lyman got the prize, there is no doubt that others deserve at least some of the credit for the successful blast of the Pottsville Furnace. Surely some should go to Benjamin Perry, the experienced ironmaster, who blew it in. Some assistance may also have been provided by David Thomas. In his letter of February 23, 1872, to B.F.H. Lynn, published in the American Manufacturer, Thomas wrote: "I received a communication from this gentleman [William Lyman] by the hand of the president of the Lehigh Crane Iron Co., for whom I was building the first furnace at this place [Catasauqua]. This letter urged me to come to Pottsville. I visited him in August, 1839, and furnished him with plans of inwall, bosh, hearth, etc., and continued to visit him about once a month until the furnace was completed . . . then I was so engaged here that I could not remain with him long enough to put it in blast. He accordingly obtained the services of Mr. B. Perry, who blew it in, as founder."

It is possible that Thomas was asked by his employer to assist Lyman because of the close relationship between the Lehigh Crane Iron Company and George Crane. James M. Swank confirmed the fact that Lyman operated the furnace under Crane's patent: "We have before us the original agreement between Robert Ralston, attorney in fact for George Crane, and William Lyman, which conveyed to the latter a license to use Crane's and Geissenhainer's patents for the use of anthracite coal in the manufacture of pig iron. It is dated at Philadelphia on December 4, 1839, and the consideration named is twenty five cents per ton of pig iron made."

The quality of iron produced at the Pottsville Furnace was described by both Firmstone and Swank as "good foundry iron;" it was produced at a rate of 28 tons per week according to Swank and 40 tons a week according to Firmstone. Johnson's assessment of this furnace's operation was somewhat more negative. At the time he visited it, probably late in 1840 or early in 1841, it was being run by the firm of Marshall, Kellogg & Company. He acknowledged the three-month successful blast that concluded in January, 1840, but commented: "Since that period several occurrences have conspired to disturb the regularity of action in this establishment." One was an attempt to heat the blast by passing a portion of it through the fire as well as over it, "thus sending in the gaseous products combustion, as well as atmospheric air, to supply the furnace. This attempt failed . . . Besides the difficulties attending the air heating apparatus, which has again given way, the Pottsville furnace has been supplied with ores of almost every variety, mixed or used separately without proper discrimination, and sometimes it is alleged the stock has become nearly or quite exhausted, leaving the works to go on without any addition of ore for hours together. It is not surprising that, under these circumstances, iron of very different qualities should be produced, and that this furnace should, with all its advantages of being situated amidst the greatest abundance of anthracite, be able to render a less satisfactory result of the anthracite iron manufacture than those which have fewer apparent advantages."

Johnson's inference is that the management of the Pottsville Furnace was both inexperienced and incompetent. According to an article printed in the Pottsville Miners' Journal, and reprinted in Mathews and Hungerford, "Mr. Lyman failed a short time after [the three-month blast]; then Mr. Marshall [of Marshall, Kellogg & Co.], now of Shamokin, ran it afterwards, and he met with the same fate. The furnace was afterwards run by other parties who had but little capital, and they too failed." The furnace was renamed the Pioneer Furnace by Dr. G.G. Palmer, who operated it in 1844. It was finally acquired by the Atkins Brothers in 1857 or 1858 and it was suggested by the writer of the article in the Pottsville Miners' Journal that they too may have met the same fate as their predecessors had it not been for the iron boom occasioned by the Civil War. According to Swank, the furnace "was practically rebuilt in 1853, torn down in 1866 and again rebuilt. In April 1888, the hot blast fell down, and the furnace was torn down in 1889 and a new furnace built in its stead."

During the spring and early summer of 1840, four more furnaces were blown in on anthracite. The Danville Furnace, built and operated by the firm of Biddle, Chambers & Company, was blown in April, 1840. It was comparatively small--as were all the anthracite furnaces built before Thomas's at Biery's Bridge--being the size of the average charcoal furnace of that period. The stack was 30 feet high, had a 7½-foot bosh and was blown through only two tuyeres. A 12-inch steam cylinder with a 4-foot stroke drove two blowing cylinders, each 40 inches in diameter with a 42-inch stroke. The blast was heated to about 600 F. The anthracite came from Wilkes-Barre via the North Branch Canal. It was supplied with both the rich (55

to 64 percent metallic iron) fossiliferous ore from Montour's Ridge
and the hard siliceous band ore mined near the works. Good quality
foundry iron was produced at a rate averaging 35 tons per week.

PIONEER FURNACE

The Pioneer Furnace at Pottsville, Pennsylvania, owned by Burd Patterson and successfully blown in by Benjamin Perry, was the first in the United States to operate
on anthracite coal alone for a three-month period. Its builder, William Lyman, was
awarded the $5,000 prize from Nicholas Biddle despite his failure to blow it in
successfully himself. Circa 1845. *From Pennsylvania History, Vol. XLI, No. 1, 1974.*

The Roaring Creek Furnace, owned by Burd Patterson & Company, was blown in by Benjamin Perry on May 18, 1840. It was located about a quarter mile upstream from the mouth of the creek on the North Branch of the Susquehanna, three miles below the town of Catawissa and five miles above Danville. The stack was 30 feet high, and had an 8½-foot bosh and three tuyeres. The site was chosen to take advantage of the valuable, but not always reliable, water power of Roaring Creek. Johnson noted, however, that while the waterwheel appeared to fulfill its purpose, it did so "imperfectly" and caused "considerable irregularity" in providing the blast. The blast was heated to 650. Like the Danville Furnace, it used anthracite from Wilkes-Barre via the North Branch Canal; fossiliferous ore was obtained from the Bloomsburg area. Production was as much as 40 tons per week of good foundry iron.

The Phoenixville Furnace, located directly on the Schuylkill Navigation about 25 miles from Philadelphia, was built in 1837 and originally worked with charcoal. The owners, Reeves, Buck & Company, then hired Julius Guiteau to erect hot-blast apparatus. Guiteau followed the same plan he had used at Mauch Chunk; the oven was situated to one side of the trunnel head where the blast was heated by the flame of the furnace to about 700. The furnace was blown in on anthracite by William Firmstone on June 17, 1840, and it remained in operation "until put out by the great flood on the 8th of January, 1841, in the Schuylkill River, which flowed into the hearth."

This venture was not wholly successful. Johnson commented: "The burning out of the hot air pipes and the destruction of the hearthstones, consequent, as is believed, on a deficient blast, have been frequent cause of embarrassment at these works." Firmstone claimed that when using all brown ore, a good soft No. 2 foundry iron was produced. Johnson agreed: "The pig metal is grey No. 2, moderately soft, but wants toughness. Bar iron, manufactured from the pig at Phoenixville, is generally cold short." Firmstone maintained that "When puddled and rolled into nail plates at the mill, [it] makes a good cut nail," provided some magnetite from the Warwick mine was mixed with the brown ores.

On July 2, 1840, the day before Thomas applied blast to his furnace, the Columbia Furnace was put into operation at Danville. In an effort to ensure success, the furnace's owner, George Patterson, had engaged Benjamin Perry to blow it in. This stack was 33 feet high and had an 8½-foot bosh diameter. A 12-inch diameter steam cylinder with a 3½-foot stroke drove two 32-inch blowing cylinders with a 5 foot, 4 inch stroke. The blast was heated to 600. The Columbia Furnace, as were most others put into blast before Thomas's, was not a complete technological success. Johnson noted:

35

"An attempt was at first made to heat the blast in a chamber above the tunnel head, but the pipes soon burned away, and leaked to such a degree as to lose a large portion of the blast. The engine was, at the same time, too small and deficient in power."

Iron production averaged 30 to 32 tons per week. "The greatest yield of iron during the first blast, which lasted only five weeks, was 5 tons in 24 hours." Johnson further commented that since the furnace manager was Benjamin Perry, "who had the care of the Pottsville Furnace during its prize blast of ninety days' continuance, and who likewise blew in the Roaring Creek Furnace, which succeeded from the first moment of its action . . . so that its want of immediate success cannot be attributed to inexperience . . . we are compelled to believe that want of sufficient blast was the main cause of the little success which attended the first trail at this establishment."

Some mention must be made of the achievements of at least two others who, while somewhat out of the mainstream of the development of anthracite technology, contributed to improvements in American ironmaking techniques. The first of these was New Jersey ironmaker Benjamin B. Howell, who took out two patents in 1828, published in the Journal of the Franklin Institute (Vol. III, February 1829, p. 138), related to making iron with anthracite and also refining iron with heated air. Howell appeared to have some success as early as 1828 in directly reducing ore in a bloomery forge using anthracite as fuel and in refining pig iron in a puddling furnace also fueled with anthracite. Some time later he claimed, in a letter dated February 24, 1838, to Dr. Thomas P. Jones, reprinted in the Journal of the Franklin Institute, to "have made good pig iron with no other fuel than anthracite." However, no specifics regarding the time and place of this achievement were offered. He did state that the circumstances surrounding their (his and his son's) accomplishment were greatly disadvantageous and it is extremely unlikely that his process was a commercially viable one. The postscript in his letter did contain a prophetic observation: "It seems to me, that the use of the hot blast is destined to revolutionize the iron manufacture."

The first application of the hot blast in the United States was undertaken by William Henry at Oxford, N.J. Henry had moved to nearby Belvidere in 1832 and to Oxford in 1834 where, under the name of William Henry & Jordan Company, he leased the Oxford Furnace for ten years. The first experiment consisted of passing waste heat at the tymp over a nest of small cast-iron pipes containing the blast. This raised the temperature to 250 and increased the furnace product by ten percent. "In 1835 a hot-blast oven, containing cast-iron arched pipes, was placed on the top of the stack by Mr. Henry and heated by the flame of the tunnel head. By this means the temperature of the blast was raised to 500. This innovation in American blast-furnace practice increased the product of the Oxford furnace by about 40 per cent, with a savings of about the same percentage of fuel. No better device for heating the blast was in use in this country until about 1840." The fuel used, however, was exclusively charcoal. Henry's activities with anthracite were to take place in Pennsylvania at Slocum Hollow (Scranton); and anthracite was not used at Oxford until some years later.

After reviewing the activities, both the successes and the failures, that preceded that propitious event at Biery's Bridge on July 4, 1840, the question must still be asked: Who contributed most to the development of the anthracite iron industry? Surely Dr. Geissenhainer deserves some of the credit, for the idea if not the accomplishment. The efforts of Baughman, Guiteau & Company were praiseworthy even though impracticable. William Lyman, however, in accepting Biddle's prize, probably got more credit than he really deserved. It is doubtful that his furnace would have succeeded without Benjamin Perry's assistance. Perry himself might have been a contender had he not flitted from furnace to furnace to aid only in the blowing-in process.

Solomon W. Roberts had no doubt who deserved the most credit. In the obituary of George Crane that he wrote for the Journal of the Franklin Institute, he stated unequivocally: "Mr. Crane is undoubtedly entitled to the honor of being the first to establish the smelting of iron with anthracite coal." Samuel Thomas, however, took issue with Solomon Roberts' assessment. Thomas noted that Mr. Crane had often received the credit of this useful discovery, then countered: "With all due respect to his memory, I must state that he was in no sense of the word a mechanic or a technical man, but a shrewd business man, with a faculty for recognizing the merits and promoting the commercial utilization of the inventions of others--a faculty, by the way, which is as essential to industrial progress as the genius of the investigator and inventor."

In support of his father, Samuel Thomas claimed that the acquisition of the machinery that Hazard had ordered for the furnace on the Lehigh was handled by his father, not by George Crane. "The real facts are, that the whole matter was placed in my father's hands, and that, during the four months he remained in Wales after signing the contract with Mr. Hazard, he made all arrangements for the entire outfit of the furnace." Samuel Thomas's arguments are most likely valid. His father was the practical man. Even if the idea of using anthracite with the hot blast had occurred to Crane alone and not to both at the same time, it was David Thomas who made it work, with far greater success than any of his contemporaries in America.

37

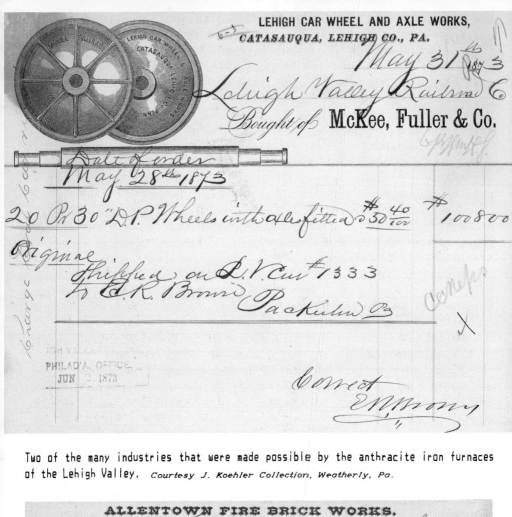

Two of the many industries that were made possible by the anthracite iron furnaces of the Lehigh Valley. *Courtesy J. Koehler Collection, Weatherly, Pa.*

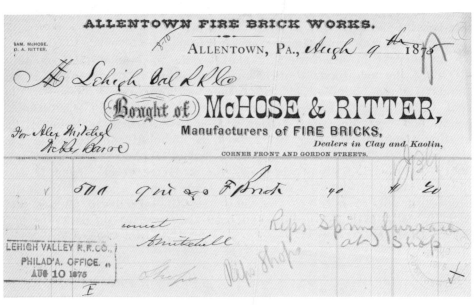

CHAPTER II

ANTHRACITE IRON AND INDUSTRIAL GROWTH IN THE LEHIGH VALLEY

The years following 1840 witnessed the nation's rapid transformation from a comparatively tranquil agrarian society to a more tumultuous industrial one. Thundering locomotives replaced the slower, more ponderous canal boats as the principal means of transportation. Huffing steam engines instead of gentle water wheels powered the new mills and factories. While some more conservative observers deplored these new developments, others saw in them romance and adventure. J.P. Lesley's description of one of the larger local furnace plants probably represents the perspective shared by most of his contemporaries:

The Allentown Iron Company's Anthracite Steam Furnaces, on the west side of the Lehigh River, one mile above Allentown in Lehigh County Pennsylvania and alongside of the Lehigh Valley Railroad, rise together from the river plane, in the grandest and most picturesque style, throwing into the shade many of the castles of Europe. No finer object of art invites the artist. The still huger pile of the Crane Works on the opposite side of the river a little higher up is rendered less striking by the vicinity of the hills; the Allentown Works rise unobstructed and unrivalled by surrounding sights, a world of stone and iron in the air, its summit crowned with tall chimneys like the turrets of Caernarvon, flames issuing from its tunnel heads, and cars travelling up and down its planes, long trains of ore mules passing to and fro across its lofty bridges, while other trains of railroad cars wait below to carry off its iron. The repose of bygone centuries seems to sit upon its immense walls, while the roaring energy of the present day fills it with a truer and better life than the revelry of Kenilworth or the chivalry of Heidelberg. Its archways conceal a perfected alchemy where the spirit of the wind converts earth to iron and dross to gold, condensing around this pile of matter a little world of intellectual and moral happiness and energy to which poets and statesmen might profitably travel to learn more than is read in books or declaimed in Congress.

Lehigh Valley businessmen and investors were quick to appreciate the potential profit in anthracite iron making. Within a few years after David Thomas's commercial success at Catasauqua, numerous other companies were formed and furnaces were soon under construction all along the Lehigh and its tributaries. At the peak of anthracite iron production, 55 blast furnaces were in operation at 21 localities throughout the greater Lehigh Valley.

ANTHRACITE FURNACES IN THE LEHIGH DISTRICT BY YEAR OF
CONSTRUCTION

Company Name	Furnace Location	Year Completed	Original Size Height	Bosh
Lehigh Crane Iron Co.	Catasauqua	No. 1 1840	45'	12'
		No. 2 1842	45'	13'4"
		No. 3 1846	47'	17'4"
		No. 4 1849	45'	18'
		No. 5 1849	45'	18'
		No. 6 1868	60'	17½'
Glendon Iron Co.	Glendon	No. 1 1844	50'	14'x18'
	(Williams Township)	No. 2 1845	45'	10'x14'
		No. 3 1850	45'	14'x16'
		No. 4 1852	47'	15'
South Easton Furnace	South Easton	No. 1 1845	48'	12'x14'
Allentown Iron Co.	Allentown	No. 1 1846	35'	12'
		No. 2 1847	35'	12'
		No. 3 1852-54	45'	16'
		No. 4 1855	50'	16'
		No. 5 1872-73	60'	17'
Durham Furnaces	Durham	No. 1 1848	40'	13'
	(Bucks County)	No. 2 1851	40'	14'
Cooper Furnaces	Phillipsburg, N.J.	No. 1 1848	55'	20'
(Trenton Iron Co.)		No. 2 1848	42'	18'
		No. 3 1848	55'	22'
Carbon Iron Co.	Parryville	No. 1 1855	40'	13'
	(Carbon County)	No. 2 1864	52'	16'
		No. 3 1869	65'	16'
Lehigh Valley Iron Co.	Coplay	No. 1 1855	45'	14'
		No. 2 1862	55'	16'
		No. 3 1868	55'	16'
Thomas Iron Co.	Hokendauqua	No. 1 1855	60'	18'
		No. 2 1855	60'	18'
		No. 3 1862	60'	18'
		No. 4 1863	60'	18'
		No. 5 1873	60'	18'
		No. 6 1874	65'	18'
Bethlehem Iron Co.	South Bethlehem	No. 1 1863	61'	16'4"
		No. 2 1867	70'	16'

Company Name	Furnace Location	Year Completed	Original Height	Size Bosh
Bethlehem Iron Co.	South Bethlehem	No. 3 1868	50'	13'
		No. 4 1874-75	70'	17½'
		No. 5 1874-75	70'	18½'
		No. 6 1881	70'	17½'
Allentown Rolling	Allentown	No. 1 1864	68'	15'
Mill Co.		No. 2 1864	68'	15'
Oxford Furnace	Oxford, N.J.	No. 1 1866	unknown	
		rebuilt 1871	63'	18'
Lock Ridge Iron Co.	Alburtis	No. 1 1868	53½'	14'
		No. 2 1869	53½'	16'
Saucon Iron Co.	Hellertown	No. 1 1869	50'	16'
		No. 2 1870	60'	16'
Lehigh Iron Co.	Aineyville	No. 1 1869	55'	16'
		No. 2 1872	60'	17'
Coleraine Iron Co.	Redington	No. 1 1869	60'	17'
	(Lower Saucon Township)	No. 2 1872	60'	17'
North Penn Iron Co.	Bingen (Lower Saucon Township)	No. 1 1870	65'	18'
Emaus Furnace	Emmaus	No. 1 1872	68'	16'
Lucy Furnace	Chain Dam (Williams Township)	No. 1 1872	65'	16'
Northampton Furnace	Shimersville (Lower Saucon Township)	No. 1 1873	64'	16'
Millerstown Iron Co.	Macungie	No. 1 1874	56'	16'
Pequest Furnace	near Oxford, N.J.	No. 1 1874	58'	16'
Hackettstown Iron & Mfg. Co.	Hackettstown, N.J.	No. 1 1875	55'	15'
Keystone Furnace	Chain Dam (Williams Township)	No. 1 1876	65'	16'

The statistics contained in this table were compiled from a variety of sources, but principally from the Directories of the American Iron and Steel Association and J.P. Lesley's The Iron Manufacturers' Guide.

One dimension is given for circular boshes, two dimensions for rectangular ones.

In the years after 1840, furnaces fueled by anthracite were built along the Schuylkill and Susquehanna rivers and in the adjoining states of New Jersey, New York, and Maryland. Anthracite ironmaking began to supplant charcoal operations wherever the canal network reached and, from the 1850s and 1860s on, wherever the railroads reached. By 1873, 46 percent of all iron produced in the United States came from anthracite furnaces, and 72 percent of these furnaces were in Pennsylvania. In that year, Pennsylvania led all other states in iron production, turning out 49 percent of the national total. As Pennsylvania led the nation, so the Lehigh Valley led Pennsylvania as the following figures illustrate:

PIG IRON PRODUCTION IN PENNSYLVANIA AS OF DECEMBER 21, 1873

District	# of Furnaces	Production in Tons
Lehigh Valley	47	389,967
Schuylkill Valley	40	236,409
Upper Susquehanna Valley	25	129,304
Lower Susquehanna Valley	37	157,403
Shenango Valley	31	160,831
Pittsburgh & Allegheny County	11	158,789

The dominant position held by the anthracite furnaces of the Lehigh and other river valleys of eastern Pennsylvania was retained for only one more decade before a gradual decline set in, the reasons for which shall be explored later. This decline was most dramatic in the Upper Susquehanna Valley but was very pronounced in the other anthracite districts as well, as can be seen in the following table:

NUMBER OF BLAST FURNACES IN PENNSYLVANIA
BY YEAR AND DISTRICT

District	1880	1884	1890	1896	1901
Lehigh	50	51	48	41	29
Schuylkill	47	44	40	26	18
Upper Susquehanna	25	23	17	7	2
Lower Susquehanna	36	37	35	21	20
Shenango	30	27	23	21	19
Allegheny (Pittsburgh)	15	16	21	27	34
Misc. Bituminous (1)	36	39	14	11	12
Juniata (2)			16	12	8
Charcoal	35	32	16	13	12
Total	274	269	230	179	154

(1)   Bituminous furnaces included those operated on coke.

(2)   Juniata Valley Furnaces were included in Misc. Bituminous category prior to 1890.

The local ironmaking boom soon had a profound effect on the character and lifestyle of the Lehigh Valley and its inhabitants. New towns and villages were established, and a number of those already in existence began to grow rapidly. Some communities owe their very origin to the iron industry. Catasauqua, called Craneville from 1839 to 1846, developed intensively around the company housing of the Crane Iron Company. In 1853 it became the first borough in Lehigh County, and throughout the second half of the nineteenth century it was second only to Allentown in importance and prosperity. For many years it was known as the Iron Borough because of the dominant role in the economic life of the borough played by the Crane furnaces and the many satellite iron-making and -forming businesses.

The establishment of the borough of Coplay was due not to the cement kilns that later made it famous, but to the furnaces built there by the Lehigh Valley Iron Company nearly two decades before David Saylor first produced portland cement nearby. The site of Hokendauqua was Thomas Butz's farm before David Thomas purchased it in 1854 for the Thomas Iron Company. In addition to building the furnace plant there, the company laid out, and for many years owned, the entire town of Hokendauqua. Before the Lock Ridge furnaces were built, Alburtis consisted of only a few homes and farms where the road from Lehigh Church to Hensingersville crossed the main line of the East Pennsylvania Railroad. Even today, the borough of Glendon is little more than the remnant of the company town built by the once-illustrious Glendon Iron Company.

Other towns and villages, such as Emmaus, Macungie, and Hellertown, while long predating the anthracite iron era, grew more rapidly and prospered after furnaces were built within or adjacent to their borders. While South Bethlehem first grew into a sizable community following completion of a zinc smelter there, it achieved real economic stature only after the construction and expansion of the Bethlehem Iron Company's furnaces and rolling mills. Allentown too changed and benefited. In addition to the furnaces and rolling mills of its two iron companies, a host of other industries became established to provide parts, equipment, and mill supplies to the furnaces, and to consume the products of the ironmakers.

The anthracite iron industry caused profound changes in the ethnic character of the Valley. Before 1840, English was rarely spoken in the rural countryside and the Pennsylvania Germans still dominated the economic, cultural, and social life of the communities. The rapid growth of the iron industry, and the related expansion of the railroads and coal mining, created more opportunities for employment than there were workers to fill them. Thus, a new wave of immigrants began to arrive. Most were from the British Isles, from England, Scotland, Wales, and Ireland. And most, especially those from England, Scotland, and Wales, had already acquired the training and experience required for the more technical and skilled jobs at the furnaces. The Irish, at least for a while after they arrived, were relegated to performing the bull work around the furnaces and building the railroads.

The new immigrants, finding the Valley attractive and its people friendly, at first tended to adapt to local customs and culture. Writing to a friend in Wales on December 11, 1839, David Thomas expressed the following observations on his new home: "We live in a fertile country where every sort of grain, vegetable and fruit is abundantly grown. The climate is very healthy; and the weather has been hitherto very good. The people are hospitable and kind, chiefly from German origin. There is much of that language spoken here, which I am learning very fast. The children can talk it better than I can."

As the years passed and they became more numerous, these immigrants increasingly began to influence the local culture. Granted their influence on the rural Pennsylvania German farmer was minimal, but in the larger towns and cities it became very considerable. It was enhanced by the fact that many of them, and their countrymen, had achieved much wealth in the iron industry and other related commercial and industrial activities. Because these immigrants were English-speaking, they had far less difficulty assimilating into the prevailing culture than the southern and eastern Europeans who were enticed to leave their homelands to work at the larger furnace plants in the 1890s and thereafter. Many of these later immigrants were never completely integrated because of the language barrier; as a result, they often lived together in close-knit communities, developing their own subcultures. Their children and grandchildren, learning English in the public schools, very quickly gained acceptance and many soon achieved positions of social and economic prominence.

The success of the iron furnaces contributed greatly to the establishment of a multitude of other industrial activities, many of which were vital to the expansion of the railroads. Indeed, the construction of the railroads and the development of the local iron industry went hand in hand, the success of one being impossible without the other. The railroads provided relatively inexpensive transportation of raw materials to the furnaces, and of the pig iron produced in them to foundries and rolling mills. The railroads in turn were for many years the largest customers for the products of the iron and steel industry. Throughout the second half of the nineteenth century an average of 50 percent of the total output of the iron and steel industry went into the manufacture of rails, locomotives, cars, and railroad bridges. This symbiotic relationship continues to exist, although within a more limited scope today. While the railroads are no longer the largest single customer of the iron and steel industry, many of the steel plants, with their huge requirements for coal and ore, could not exist without the railroads.

For many years, one of the principal products of the mills of the Bethlehem Iron Company and the Allentown Rolling Mill Company was rolled iron rails. The Allentown mills also produced other railroad products including track spikes and plates, and car axles. Their shops turned out mine- and flat cars. Other companies, devoted exclusively to manufacturing railroad products and rolling stock from locally produced pig and rolled iron, were soon established in Lehigh County. One such firm was Frederick & Company, founded in 1866 by Thomas Frederick, Charles F. Beck and A. Wisser to manufacture railroad cars. Their foundry and car shops were built along the main line of the Lehigh Valley Railroad a mile south of West Catasauqua, at a place then known as Ferndale, now Fullerton, Whitehall Township. The firm employed more than 200 persons before it failed during the depression of the mid 1870s. One of the largest of the railroad product suppliers in Lehigh County was the carwheel works built in 1866 by James W. Fuller and James McKee. This firm, known as McKee, Fuller & Company until 1901 when it was incorporated as the Lehigh Car Wheel and Axle Works, was formed originally to manufacture only car wheels. It grew slowly until 1880, when Fuller succeeded in obtaining a contract from the Erie Railroad to build 1,849 eight-wheeled railroad cars. In order to complete this contract, McKee and Fuller purchased the vacant Frederick car shops which adjoined the south end of their plant and also installed a forge shop to make their own axles. By 1884, the firm employed 1,500 workers and its sales reached $4,000,000 per annum. In 1891 car-building was discontinued and the firm began manufacturing crushing machinery as the Lehigh Fuller Pulverizing Mills. The reorganized successor to this firm, the Fuller Company, now occupies the former site of the once-famous Crane Iron Company. Another local car-building firm was the Lehigh Car Manufacturing Company, located along the Central Railroad of New Jersey tracks at Stemton, Allen Township, Northampton County, across the bridge from Coplay. During the 1870s this firm was engaged in the manufacture of box, gondola, ore, and mine cars.

Other iron-using establishments included foundries, machine shops, and boiler works. Some, like the East Penn Foundry in Emmaus (later merged into the cast iron pipe works of the Donaldson Iron Company), and the Millerstown Foundry in Macungie, were located in the smaller communities of the Valley, but most were located nearer the larger furnace plants at Allentown and Catasauqua. The Union Steam Boiler Works, located at Front and Linden streets in Allentown, were built in 1863 by James B. Cole and Abiel Heilman. This

The Millerstown Foundry was typical of the many small operations that consumed locally produced pig iron. It was built in the mid 1870s by James Miller and was
operated by Miller and his sons until it was destroyed by a series of fires in 1911.
Pig iron from the adjacent Macungie Furnace is stacked outside the cupola building,
where it will be remelted to produce a variety of iron castings including bakeoven
doors, stove and pump parts, and plows. Circa 1887. *Courtesy Elizabeth W. Moatz.*

The Donaldson Iron Company's pipe foundry in Emmaus, Lehigh County, circa 1900. The
foundry was built by the lessees of the Emaus Furnace in 1883 and operated in conjunction with the furnace until 1890, when Robert H. Coleman acquired the lease for
the furnace. Thereafter both were operated as independent enterprises. Foundry
operations continued until 1943, and the company was dissolved in 1947. *Courtesy
Lehigh County Historical Society.*

firm, known as Cole and Heilman until Cole died in 1883 after which it became the Heilman Boiler Works, manufactured locomotive boilers and tanks, and items such as cylindrical, vertical, and flue boilers, stacks, standpipes, and blast and steam pipes that were used at the local iron furnaces.

The Allentown Boiler Works, situated between the Lehigh Valley Railroad and the Central Railroad of New Jersey near Hamilton Street, was founded by Charles Collum in 1883. This company manufactured a product line similar to that of Cole and Heilman at first, but later concentrated on cement-mill equipment after that industry began to gain prominence. Barber & Son, proprietors of the Allentown Foundry and Machine Works on the river side of the Lehigh Valley Railroad depot, manufactured steam engines, boilers, and mill gearing. W.F. Mosser & Company, located until recently at its original site at Second and Union streets, was founded in 1863 as the Lehigh Valley Axle Works to produce carriage and wagon axles. The other partners in the firm soon dropped out and William F. Mosser conducted the business himself until 1890 when his son was admitted to the firm. By the 1870s Mosser had expanded the firm's product line to include steam engines, furnace castings, mill gearing, and the Eureka turbine waterwheel which rapidly replaced the wooden overshot wheels in many of the Valley's mills during the 1870s and 1880s. Later, A.N. Wolf, the patent holder, licensed Barber & Son to produce the Eureka turbine; Mosser countered by manufacturing his own improved model known as the Allentown Turbine Waterwheel. The firm of Albright, Son & Company, still located at Front and Linden streets in Allentown, was founded by Phaon Albright over 100 years ago to manufacture wrought iron and brass pipe, fittings, and specialties. Albright and Son custom-made many of the tuyeres and other fittings for the iron furnaces throughout the Valley.

The Catasauqua Manufacturing Company operated rolling mills both at Ferndale (Fullerton) and adjacent to the Crane Iron Company in Catasauqua. The Catasauqua mill was built in 1863 by the Northern Iron Company, the officers of which were David Thomas, president, Charles G. Earp, secretary, and David Eynon, superintendent. The founders' intent was to produce armor plate for naval vessels but the Civil War ended before production was under way and the plant was modified to produce tank and boiler plate, and sheet iron. The Ferndale mill was built in 1864 by the East Penn Iron Company to roll bar and skelp iron; the name was later changed to the Lehigh Manufacturing Company. In 1868 the owners of the Catasauqua mill changed their firm's name to the Catasauqua Manufacturing Company and in the same year leased the Ferndale mill, purchasing it outright in 1872. The plants were run by David Thomas, his sons Samuel and John, and Oliver Williams, a large share holder. Williams served as general manager from 1867 until 1879, when he succeeded David Thomas as president. He served in that capacity until 1892, when a strike and the general panic of that year combined to force the once nationally famous mill into bankruptcy.

The Davies and Thomas Foundry, located along Race Street in Catasauqua, had a rather inauspicious beginning before finally achieving national prominence during the late nineteenth and early twentieth centuries. It was founded in 1865 by Daniel Davies and William Thomas, two Welshmen formerly associated with the Crane Iron Company. The firm was operated as a partnership until 1867, when Thomas, who was related to neither the David Thomas nor the Hopkin Thomas families, returned to Wales. It was carried on by Daniel Davies and his son George until 1876, when the elder Davies died. Because of then-prevailing poor business conditions, the foundry was shut down until 1879 when James Thomas, son of Hopkin Thomas and brother-in-law to George Davies, purchased a half-interest and reopened the plant. For the next 40 years the firm prospered under the direction of these two men and their progeny.

This foundry, which often employed as many as 600 men, produced 80 percent of the huge cast iron plates used to line the various tunnels connecting Manhattan Island with Long Island and with northern New Jersey. It was by far the major supplier of castings for the construction of the subways in New York, Philadelphia, Washington, D.C., and Baltimore. For many years it was also the principal supplier of castings used in the construction of water and coal-gas plants built by A.O. Granger and the United Gas Improvement Company during the late nineteenth and early twentieth centuries.

The Bryden Horse Shoe Company was organized in 1882 with Joshua Hunt, son-in-law of David Thomas, as president and Oliver Williams, then president of the Catasauqua Manufacturing company, as secretary and treasurer. It was established essentially to serve as a consumer of the rolled iron bar produced by the neighboring rolling mills. At first, production was concentrated on shoes for street-car horses, manufactured under the patent of George Bryden of Hartford, Connecticut. As electrified cars replaced horse-drawn ones in the 1890s the product line was expanded to include shoes of all types. As the business grew, it provided employment for more than 300 men and produced 50 tons of forged shoes daily. In 1928 the firm was purchased by the Phoenix Manufacturing Company of Joliet, Illinois, and the product line was diversified to include various types of commercial closed-die forgings, especially forged pipe and tank flanges, the principal products manufactured there today.

The Davies and Thomas Foundry in Catasauqua designed and manufactured cast iron tunnel segments that were used in the construction of tunnels under the Hudson and East rivers in New York Harbor, and for several subway systems on the east coast. This photo may depict the visit of officials from New York to inspect an assembled tunnel section. Circa 1895. *Courtesy A. Newton Bugbee, Jr.*

In 1851, nine years before he embarked upon his illustrious career at the Bethlehem Iron Company, John Fritz, together with his brother George and brothers-in-law B.F. Stroud and Isaac E. Chandler, established an iron foundry adjacent to the Crane furnace at Front Street and Pine. This was the first foundry in the Lehigh Valley, and one of the first in the nation, to produce cast iron columns for construction purposes. After Fritz moved to Johnstown in 1854 to serve as superintendent of the Cambria Iron Works, the foundry was acquired by David Thomas who in turn sold it to Oliver Williams, David Williams and William Hopkins in 1869. In 1905 the company failed and the plant was acquired by Leonard Peckitt, president of the Empire Steel and Iron Company.

Until 1854, all the refractory brick required to line the furnaces and stoves of the local iron furnaces was imported from Europe or elsewhere in the United States. However in that year Samuel McHose, the mason who supervised the construction of nearly all the early furnaces throughout the Lehigh Valley, and Oliver A. Ritter established a fire-brick factory at the foot of Gordon Street

49

in Allentown. The firm operated as McHose and Ritter until 1874, when David Saylor purchased McHose's interest; it was then renamed Saylor and Ritter. Later, Eugene Gardiner purchased Saylor's interest and the business continued as Ritter & Gardiner until it went out of business in 1900. In its early years this firm employed up to 100 workers and manufactured as many as 3,500,000 firebrick annually.

In 1873 Joseph Downing and a Mr. Lewis founded the Industrial Fire Brick Company in East Allentown. In 1875 Downing became sole owner for 20 years, after which the business was carried on by his nephew, William Downing, who continued production into the second decade of this century. The Lehigh Fire Brick Works was established in Catasauqua in 1868 by Samuel McHose, Oliver A. Ritter and David Thomas. In 1873 Ritter and McHose sold out to David Thomas who then brought his sons Samuel and John and son-in-law Joshua Hunt into the firm. The original plant burned in 1872 and was replaced by stone structures built along the canal between F.W. Wint and the Bryden Horse Shoe Works. This brick yard continued to manufacture common refractories for iron furnaces, stoves, coke ovens, cupolas, and kilns into the early years of the twentieth century. The stone structures were only recently torn down by the Phoenix Forging Company.

It would be difficult to overemphasize the importance of the role played by anthracite ironmaking in the continuing development of the iron and steel industry. While it was certainly not the ultimate technology, the development of new practices and machinery by the ironmakers of this era established the foundations on which all subsequent improvements were based. In 1810, of the 153 blast furnaces in the United States, 50 were in Pennsylvania. The total iron production of these furnaces was 53,908 tons of which over half, or 26,870 tons, was produced in the state. The average output per furnace was only 352 tons per year. By 1840 the number of furnaces had increased to 804, of which 213 were in Pennsylvania. Total U.S. production in 1840 was 286,903 tons; 98,395 tons were produced in Pennsylvania. While total production had increased five-fold, the average production per furnace had risen only to 357 tons. After 1840, production increased dramatically. By 1847 the 304 furnaces in Pennsylvania produced 389,350 tons of pig iron, more than was produced in the whole country only seven years earlier. That the use of anthracite was largely responsible for this tremendous increase becomes obvious from a review of the following figures:

1885 view of the Abbott Street industrial area. Developed by the Lehigh Coal and Navigation Company in 1832, by 1840 it contained 12 water-powered industrial sites, employing over one thousand men. *Canal Museum-Hugh Moore Park Collection, Easton,*

Lehigh Port on the right bank of the Lehigh River in Allentown was developed from the 1840s as a transfer point for goods and materials, and as an early industrial area. This view from the 1870s shows the boat basin and several water-powered industries. *Courtesy Lehigh County Historical Society.*

51

BLAST FURNACES IN PENNSYLVANIA IN 1847

	No.	1847 Production	Average Tons per Furnace
Anthracite coal	57	151,331	2,655 tons
Bituminous coal	7	7,800	1,114 tons
Coke	4	10,000	2,500 tons
Charcoal, hot blast	85	94,519	1,112 tons
Charcoal, cold blast	145	125,155	863 tons
Bloomeries	6	545	91 tons
TOTAL	304	389,350	

However, despite the higher output of the anthracite-fueled furnaces, the larger number of charcoal furnaces scattered throughout the rural countryside continued to produce a larger share of the nation's iron until 1855. In that year anthracite iron production in the United States, 381,866 tons, for the first time exceeded charcoal production, 339,922 tons. As more anthracite furnaces were built their percentage of the total iron production in the United States continued to increase. By the time of the Civil War, the anthracite furnaces of eastern Pennsylvania were producing nearly half of the nation's iron. During this period the Lehigh Valley alone produced slightly more than 20 percent of the national total.

The dominant position of the anthracite iron industry continued until 1875 when the bituminous coal- and coke-fueled furnaces in the western part of the state for the first time outproduced the older anthracite stacks east of the Susquehanna River. While anthracite production tripled during the closing quarter of the nineteenth century, the output of the newer and larger coke furnaces grew even more spectacularly, to a level eight times that of the anthracite furnaces by the turn of the century. This trend is vividly illustrated in the following table:

PRODUCTION OF IRON IN THE U.S.
BY PRINCIPAL FUELS IN SELECTED YEARS

Years– net tons	Anthracite	Charcoal	Bituminous and coke	Total
1854	339,435	342,298	54,485	736,218
1855	381,866	339,922	62,390	784,178
1860	519,211	278,331	122,228	919,770
1866	749,367	332,580	268,396	1,350,343
1869	971,150	392,150	553,341	1,916,641
1875	908,046	410,990	947,545	2,266,581
1880	1,807,651	537,558	1,950,205	4,295,414
1886	2,099,597	459,557	3,806,174	6,365,328
1890	2,448,781	703,522	7,154,725	10,307,028
1896	3,156,487	1,098,550	13,118,600	17,373,637
1901	3,190,087	706,750	20,771,200	24,812,037

Lock Ridge Furnace as it appeared in the 1904 stockholders report of the Thomas Iron Company. Stack No. 7 is on the right; No. 8 is on the left. The four Durham-style pipe stoves that heated the blast for No. 7 stack are to its right. Vertical elevators were used to carry the filling barrows to the dumping ring at the furnace top. The Massasoit is standing in front of the three stockhouses.

Interior view, circa 1910, of Durham pipe stove with all pipes removed. The hammers held by some of the workers were used to break the cast iron sleeves that held the U-shaped pipes to the heavy bed-pipe hubs projecting from the floor. The connection between the light-weight sleeves, the U-pipe, and the hubs was made airtight by a rust joint. This joint was made by mixing iron borings or chips with sal ammoniac into a thick paste which was caulked into the cavity between the three components, creating rapid oxidation that caused the borings to expand, completely sealing the joint. *Courtesy William Schlechter.*

CHAPTER III

LOCK RIDGE FURNACE
AN EXAMPLE OF THE TECHNOLOGY OF
ANTHRACITE IRONMAKING

The partially restored ruins of the Lock Ridge furnaces at Alburtis in southwestern Lehigh County represent the best-preserved remnant of the anthracite iron industry. The county park and museum that now occupy the site provide visitors an opportunity to experience and appreciate the ironmaking activities that once dominated the industrial landscape of the Lehigh Valley.

While the park and museum are still owned by Lehigh County, the Lehigh County Historical Society has been charged with the administration of the museum since the early 1980s. Restoration of the site was begun in the early 1970s and completed by the Bicentennial in 1976. Unfortunately, work was undertaken without a comprehensive archaeological investigation of the site and the details of some of the plant's operations are still not fully understood. In addition, no attempt was made to restore the property authentically; in fact, adaptive reuse is perhaps a better description than restoration. In recent years funds for maintenance have been minimal and there has been considerable deterioration to the physical plant.

While the Lock Ridge Furnace was never a major iron plant, it is representative of the many merchant pig-iron furnaces built during the anthracite iron era. It is situated along the right-of-way of the Catasauqua and Fogelsville Railroad, which was built jointly by the Crane Iron Company of Catasauqua and the Thomas Iron Company of Hokendauqua to convey the brown hematite ores of western Lehigh County to their furnaces along the banks of the Lehigh River. Construction was begun in 1856 and the roadbed completed to Rupp's Station on July 14, 1857. Near Troxels, in South Whitehall Township, the railroad crossed the Jordan Creek Valley via the "Iron Bridge." This locally famous wrought-iron bridge was 1,165 feet long and rose 104 feet above the streambed. By the early twentieth century it became obsolete, unable to safely bear the weight of newer, heavier locomotives pulling cars of greatly increased capacity. Beginning in the summer of 1916 and continuing through 1919, the Philadelphia and Reading Railway Company, in cooperation with the Crane and Thomas iron companies, systematically dumped more than 300,000 tons of gravel, fly-ash, and slag fill over the structure, covering it completely. Track crews then laid heavier, stronger rails over the massive embankment thus created.

In 1864, the Catasauqua and Fogelsville Railroad was extended southwards to the junction of the East Pennsylvania Railroad at what is now Alburtis, and in 1865 it was extended farther to Rittenhouse Gap and to Red Lion in Berks County, to reach the magnetite ore deposits discovered in that area.

It was not until after the completion of the Catasauqua and Fogelsville Railroad that the construction of a blast furnace at Lock Ridge became economically feasible. While the plant's location was convenient to the magnetite deposits at Rittenhouse Gap and the limonite deposits throughout Lower Macungie Township, the railroad was essential for the transportation of anthracite coal to the furnace.

The decision to build at Lock Ridge was probably made as early as March 29, 1864, when a group of Thomas Iron Company officials, including David Thomas, Samuel Thomas, Joshua Hunt, John Thomas, and John Williams, purchased a tract of land consisting of 88 acres and 101 perches southeast of the intersection of the Catasauqua and Fogelsville and East Pennsylvania railroads from George Clauss for the sum of $10,635.75. They resold the same tract to the Lock Ridge Iron Company on March 4, 1867, for $11,700. The Lock Ridge Iron Company had been chartered a few months earlier, on December 26, 1866, with Samuel Thomas as president and J.H. Knight as secretary-treasurer, the same positions that they held with the Thomas Iron Company.

Construction began in 1867 and the first furnace was put into blast on March 18, 1868; the second furnace was blown in on July 9, 1869. These furnaces were later designated No. 7 and No. 8. Soon after the first furnace was successfully in blast the entire capital stock of the Lock Ridge Iron Company was acquired at par value on May 1, 1869, by the Thomas Iron Company. During the fifty-four years that this plant was in operation it generally produced iron at a lower cost than most of the other Thomas furnaces despite the fact that its facilities were seldom as modern.

The original furnace stacks were constructed along much the same lines as furnaces No. 1 and No. 2 at Hokendauqua, having massive stones bases of traditional shape, reinforced with iron rods running diagonally between adjacent sides. The stacks were 46 feet square at their base and tapered slightly toward the top. The upper portion of the stack was fabricated from iron plates reinforced both vertically and horizontally around the circumference with iron bars. The entire stack was lined with firebrick two or more courses thick. The thickness was related to the particular zone within the furnace and the activity occurring at that level, the heaviest lining being in the crucible or hearth area which contained the molten iron and cinder. Fireclay was placed into a small gap left between the firebrick and the supporting structure at either the stone base or the iron shell at the top, to absorb the expansion of the refractory lining when the furnace was put into blast. The brick lining at the top was anchored to the supporting framework by tie bolts that were embedded between the rows of brick and passed through the iron shell plates to which they were attached.

No. 7 furnace had a bosh diameter of 14 feet and the bosh diameter of No. 8 stack was 16 feet. Both furnaces were 53 feet, 6 inches high when originally constructed. In December 1875, No. 7 stack was raised to 60 feet; by 1881, the height of No. 8 stack was also 60 feet. These dimensions then remained more or less constant until 1914 and 1915 when extensive renovations were undertaken. The hot-blast main, the large refractory-lined pipe which carried the heated blast air from the stoves, entered the arch nearest the pipe stoves and was connected to the bustle pipe, which encircled the stack between the outer supporting masonry and the refractory lining. The original number of tuyeres is unknown; however, it is known that by August 1881, No. 8 furnace had "7 tuyeres all pointing toward the center, and 8 feet from point to point of tuyere."

It was during this time, the summer of 1881, that major modifications were made to No. 8 furnace that eventually resulted in significant changes in the configuration of all other Thomas Iron Company furnaces. The series of events leading to the modification in stack design began when, in an effort to improve operating efficiency, a "Lurman Front" or cinder notch was installed to replace the old-style open front. This consisted of a set of water-jacketed castings, fitted together as a single unit and inserted into the brickwork at a level a foot so below the tuyere line of the furnace. Its purpose was to allow the cinder or slag to be tapped off at intervals between iron taps. This cinder notch was located 90 degrees from the tap hole or iron notch at a level approximately three feet higher. When the cinder notch was later installed at No. 7 furnace, it was located in the archway that is now the main entrance to the furnace museum. During normal furnace operations, the fluxing action of the limestone would cause slag or cinder containing the impurities removed from the ore to float on top of the molten iron in the hearth. As the hearth filled with molten metal and the cinder level rose nearly to the tuyeres, the cinder was tapped off through the notch to prevent damage to the tuyeres. This was accomplished by removing the refractory plug from the water cooled notch casting and allowing the cinder to run off through a sand-lined trough into a cinder car for transfer to the dump. By tapping the cinder off between iron taps, a greater volume of iron could be accumulated in the hearth, larger pours could be made, and the time between casts lengthened. By having the furnace "in blast" for longer periods, production was increased.

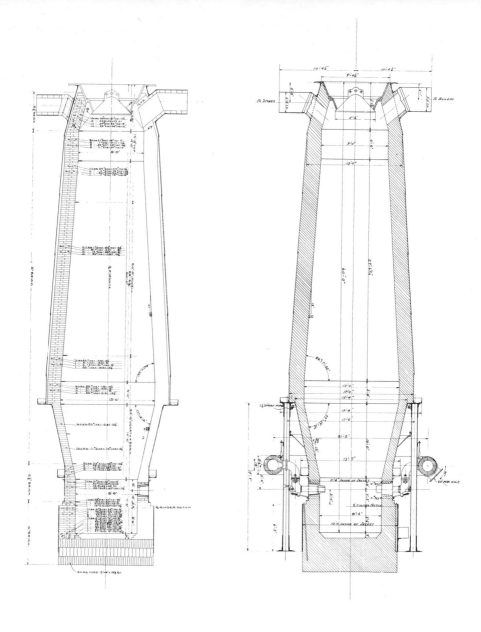

Contractor's drawing of No. 7 stack as rebuilt in 1915. Brickwork is detailed in drawing on left; tuyere placement, bustle pipe location and mantle support posts are shown in drawing on right. The bell and hopper and gas offtakes are at the top of the stack. *Arthur G. McKee, Engineer, Cleveland, Ohio.*

58

Concurrent with the installation of the Lurman front, the tuyeres were raised from levels of 3½ and 4 feet above the hearth bottom to a uniform height of 5 feet above the bottom. Within a month after these changes were made, No. 8 furnace began behaving in a very unusual manner. David H. Thomas, who was superintendent at Lock Ridge at the time these changes were made, described them a few years later at a meeting of the American Institute of Mining Engineers:

I had a very successful blow-in, in the month of August, 1881. Everything worked well and gave satisfaction to all, until the fourth week, when the furnace began to work very gray, and the consumption of fuel came down from 1 ton 12 cwt. to 1 ton 6 cwt. per ton of iron. This week ended with the 1 a.m. cast Saturday. On the following Sunday the first fine-dirt trouble ever experienced in any of the Thomas Iron Company's furnaces began. The 7 a.m. cast on Sunday was No. 1 and No. 2 iron. When the blast was taken off after casting the furnace made a drop of 5 feet, and when the blast was again put on, the pressure on the engine had risen 2 pounds, and the gas was very dirty, covering the boiler with a brown deposit. The stock began slipping instead of sinking steadily. In all the slipping or dropping the stock always remained level. As soon as the cinder rose to the tuyeres they began to work dirty and dark and the cinder changed from a light gray to a heavy dark. At the next cast, at 1 p.m., the iron was No. 2 mill, and at 7 p.m., white. After putting on the blast after the last cast, things began to look serious. The pressure rose to 12 pounds, and the furnace stopped making gas. The blast was on for four hours before any sign of cinder appeared at the tuyeres. We tried to tap, but found neither iron nor cinder at either the cinder or the iron notch. From this time, in spite of everything we did, we lost all the tuyeres except the front one, which was over the dam and 2 feet 6 inches to the left of the cinder-notch. The blast was then shut off from all the tuyeres except the front one. The cinder-block and water-box were removed, and by hard work the front tuyere was kept working throughout this trouble, which lasted for 24 hours. At the end of this time, some fresh stock came down to the tuyere; the furnace began melting; the pressure went down to 8 pounds, and gas appeared under the boilers and in the hot-blast again. At the end of another 24 hours, the furnace was making No. 2 and No. 3 iron, and tuyeres all working bright.

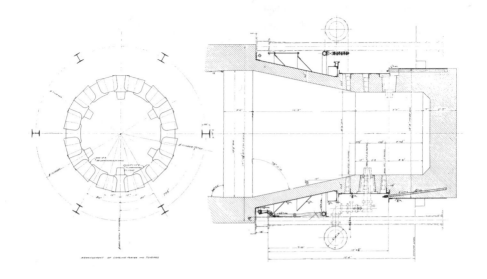

Drawing of hearth and bosh cooling system after last modification.

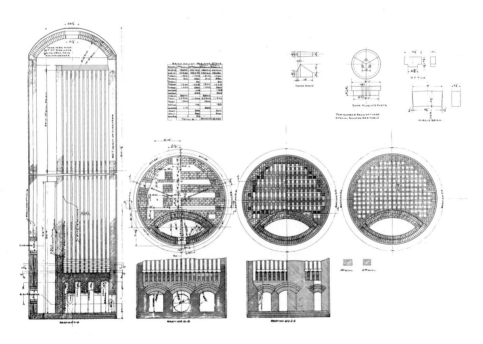

Contractor's drawing showing refractory details of McKee-Nelson regenerative stoves completed in 1915.

This trouble came every four or five weeks for six months. I tried everything I could think of or hear of, but all seemed to end in the same way. At last, thinking that the stock was not properly distributed and that the furnace was working up the center, I pulled back the tuyeres and had all the fine hematite ore dumped in the center of the furnace and coarser material to the sides. This was done by swinging the bell. When the effect of this change arrived at the tuyeres, the cinder turned black and the iron white. The furnace showed all the symptoms of another dirt-trouble; and this lasted for 36 hours, but without causing the loss of any tuyeres.

The furnace began to work better again, making foundry-iron, but at the expense of fuel, as it took 1 ton 14 cwt. of coal to the ton of iron. I again changed the mode of filling by dumping every other charge to the center and increasing the amount of fuel put in at one time, so as to have a layer of coal and of ore and stone all across the furnace from 8 to 10 inches thick. I found 5400 pounds of fuel put in at one time did the best work in furnaces Nos. 7 and 8. No. 8 was in blast one year after this last change, making from 25 to 30 tons more iron that she ever did before, and with less fuel, without any more signs of trouble from fine dirt. At the end of the year the furnace was blown out on account of dull times, and was found to have burnt herself to the shape shown in figure 8. Thinking the altered shape of the furnace had had much to do with our getting rid of the dirt-trouble, I consulted with Mr. John Thomas, the general manager, and Mr. William Thomas, the superintendent of the Thomas Iron Company; and it was decided to pull the tuyeres back on No. 7 and re-line No. 2, and make her the same shape as No. 8 had burnt to. Up to this time the best average work on the Lock Ridge furnace had been 260 tons per week for six months; and the best at the Hokendauqua furnaces had been 288 tons per week. After putting the tuyeres back on No. 7, she made an average for six months of 308½ tons, 70 per cent, being foundry iron, and made only 6½ tons of mottled in one year. . . . After this all furnaces of the Thomas Iron Company, when blown out for repairs were re-lined to the same lines as Nos. 8 and 2, and as this was done the output, both quantity and quality were increased and the amount of fuel to the ton of iron decreased, and the fine dirt problem disappeared.

For many years after this, few changes were made to the furnace stacks and production remained fairly constant. The introduction of the Durham stoves, described later, did increase production somewhat, but it was not until 1914-1915 that major changes were made to the furnace plant. This major rehabilitation of the Lock Ridge facilities was undertaken during the administration of Ralph H. Sweetser, who succeeded B.F. Fackenthal, Jr. upon Fackenthal's resignation on May 1, 1913. Sweetser's decision to embark upon this project was directly opposed to Fackenthal's own recommendations to modernize the Thomas Iron Company which he presented to the Board of Directors when he resigned. Fackenthal favored a policy of modest retrenchment and suggested that facilities be concentrated at Hokendauqua. He advised the directors: "I would not spend another dollar at Alburtis, after making another blast at No. 8, when the works should be abandoned."

Fortunately for the workers at Lock Ridge, Fackenthal's advice, which may have been in the long-run corporate best interest, went unheeded and Sweetser spent considerable quantities of money at Alburtis. No. 8 stack was the first to be remodeled, the work being performed during the summer of 1914. The results of this rebuilding were considered so encouraging that in their annual report submitted on June 8, 1915, the Board of Directors announced that they had authorized the rebuilding of No. 7 furnace along the same lines at No. 8. These rebuilds consisted of constructing entirely new steel-jacketed furnace stacks within the old stone base. The bulk of the weight of these new stacks was supported by six hollow steel posts reinforced inside with a wide flanged beam and with concrete poured into the remaining voids. In order to fit the new steel jacketed stack inside the old masonry base, the configuration of the stack had to be modified considerably. The bosh diameter of both No. 7 and No. 8 furnaces was reduced to 13 feet and the inside diameter of the hearth was reduced to 8½ feet; the stack height remained 60 feet. The tuyere height was raised to 6½ feet above the hearth bottom; the cinder notch was raised to 4 feet 3 inches, leaving a distance of 2 feet 3 inches between the cinder notch and tuyeres. Six tuyeres were installed equidistantly around the circumference.

In order to cool the thin refractory lining and protect the steel jacket from breakouts, three methods of cooling were employed on that section of the stack below the point where it was tied into the old stone stack. A 2½ inch diameter spray pipe was installed just below the tie-in point, at a level approximately 19 feet above the base of the supporting posts. This pipe completely encircled the bosh jacket and had 3/16 inch diameter spray holes drilled into it on 2 inch centers. The cooling water was pumped through this pipe and the spray was directed against the top of the bosh jacket and allowed to run down the outside of the steel shell to provide the required cooling action.

In the tuyere zone, water-jacketed copper cooling plates were set into the refractory work to cool the adjoining area. In the hearth area, stave cooling was employed. This consisted of heavy cast iron or cast steel plates 3 inches thick with 1¼ inch diameter pipes cast inside. They were inserted into the refractory lining at intervals 14½ inches apart around the hearth diameter. Cooling water was pumped continuously through both the cooling plates and staves, which helped to prolong the life of the brick lining. The drawings accompanying this test were provided by the Arthur G. McKee Company of Cleveland, Ohio, which performed this work under contract for the Thomas Iron Company. Contract No. 197 covered the complete remodeling of No. 7 stack. Contract No. 256 covered the installation of a new bosh jacket and a reline of No. 8 stack. The drawings relating to the original modification of No. 8 stack, which was performed in 1914, have been lost.

STOVES

Three generations of hot blast stoves were employed at Lock Ridge over its fifty-four year span of operation. The original stoves, constructed in 1867, were Thomas-design iron pipe stoves similar to those used at the Crane Iron Company and the Thomas Hokendauqua plant. In 1891 four Durham-style iron pipe stoves were installed for No. 7 furnace and in 1910 Durham stoves were also added to No. 8 furnace. In a last-ditch effort to modernize and increase both efficiency and productivity, two McKee-Nelson regenerative stoves were added to No. 7 furnace in 1914-15, two of the four Durham stoves being retained as preheaters.

During the heyday of anthracite ironmaking in the Lehigh Valley the iron pipe stove was in nearly universal use. It was not until the 1870s that any regenerative stoves were constructed in the Valley and it was not until 1891, when three regenerative stoves, each 18 feet in diameter by 65 feet high, were added to No. 6 furnace at Hokendauqua, that the Thomas Iron Company made any effort to utilize this more modern design. The pipe stoves had the advantage of being relatively inexpensive and simple to construct and could be operated continuously as long as the furnace was producing gas. The first Lock Ridge pipe stoves consisted of a single large red-brick chamber, lined on the inside with firebrick. Beneath the brick or tile floor passed horizontal pipes with nozzles or connections on their top surface and a vertical partition in their central plane. Connected to the nozzles were pairs of "U" shaped pipes reaching practically to the top of the chamber, through which the blast air had to pass on its path from the blowing engine to the furnace tuyeres. The vertical partition in the horizontal bed pipes prevented the blast air from by-passing the "U" pipes which were connected in series. The chamber containing the iron pipes was centrally located within the stove structure; the combustion chamber was at one end and the draft stack at the other. The gas generated by normal furnace operations was tapped off by a flue constructed near the top of the furnace stack and conveyed via the "downcomer" to the stove's combustion chamber where it was burned. The draft created by the tall stove stack at the opposite end of the pipe chamber drew the burning gases across the rows of pipes, through the slits in the end of the chamber and on up the stack. A baffle wall, with openings in its base, was constructed in the middle of the chamber to prevent the gas from passing along the top of the stove to the stack without passing down around the pipes. By forcing the gas current to the bottom of the chamber in this manner, a good distribution of the intensely hot products of combustion over the surface of the pipes was assured. Passing through this series of heated "U" pipes, the cold blast air became progressively hotter before entering the refractory-lined hot blast main which carried it to the bustle pipe for distribution to the individual tuyeres. The floor of the pipe chamber was covered with fire tile to protect the horizontal bed pipe from damage from the hot gases.

The Durham stoves constructed for No. 7 furnace in 1891 were not of the most efficient design for the consumption of furnace gas, but their design did allow for higher blast temperatures and lower maintenance than did the more efficient Glendon stoves. The principal difference between the Durham and the Glendon stoves, named for the Lehigh Valley furnaces where they were developed, was not so much in their construction but rather in the direction in which the blast air passed through the pipes.

In the Glendon stove the cold air entered at the draft stack end of the stove and progressed through increasing temperatures to the combustion-chamber end where it was discharged to the hot blast main; the opposite air flow was followed in the Durham stove. The maximum blast temperature in the Glendon stove had to be limited to no more than 850 degrees because by the time the heated blast air reached the pipes next to the hot combustion chamber end of the stove, the air was already heated to nearly the maximum temperature limit of the stove. If more gas were burned in an effort to raise the blast temperature any higher, those pipes next to the combustion chamber, being most directly exposed to the intense heat and flames entering from that chamber, would quickly deteriorate, distort out of shape and eventually rupture, thereby shutting down the furnace.

The regenerative stoves shared a common draft stack. Two of the Durham pipe stoves were retained as preheaters, one in use and one as a spare. Circa 1917. *Courtesy Charles Eisenhard.*

View of the Lock Ridge works showing the 132-foot standpipe for the hydraulic hoisting mechanism. The two larger-diameter stacks framed by the elevator structures provided draft for the two boiler plants that were on top of the blowing engine house. The single-chamber Thomas pipe stoves can be seen to the left of No. 8 stack. A portion of the plant's huge slag banks looms in the background. *C.L. Bartholomew Collection.*

In the Durham stove the cold air first entering the hottest pipes next to the combustion-chamber end cooied those pipes to such an extent that more gas could be burned and a higher overall blast temperature achieved. The principal deficiency of this type of stove is that the waste gases had to pass off at a temperature 200 to 300 degrees higher than that of the hot blast air they were discharging, otherwise the last rows of pipes were worthless, being incapable of transferring any heat. In the Glendon stove, on the other hand, the hot gas could be discharged at a temperature several hundred degrees lower and still transfer heat to the blast air entering the stack end.

Most pipes employed elliptically shaped pipes with the broad side of the ellipse exposed to the direct current of burning or heated gases. By exposing a larger surface area directly to the products of combustion, this pipe configuration allowed for greater heat transfer through the pipe and increased the gas efficiency of the stove. The elliptical section somewhat constricted the air flow; since the blast pressure was constant, this increased the velocity of the blast air as it passed through the pipe, thereby increasing the heat transfer efficiency. The principal difficulty with the elliptical shape was that because of its narrow cross section, it was prone to bend and twist around much more than a circular cross-section pipe, especially at the combustion-chamber end of the furnace. Thus stove temperatures had to be maintained at a lower level if downtime for pipe replacement were to be minimized. It is very probable that the circular cross-section design was chosen for the Lock Ridge stoves for this reason, to achieve high blast temperatures and still retain low maintenance levels. Also, the efficient use of furnace gas was probably not a prime concern to the operators of Lock Ridge.

Blast furnace practice for most nineteenth century anthracite furnaces was such that far more gas was generated than was required to heat the stoves and produce steam for the blowing engines and other miscellaneous steam-operated equipment around the furnace. The gas not burned for these purposes was allowed to pass off into the atmosphere or was burned off. It was primarily at the newer integrated steel plants, such as the one then taking shape at Bethlehem, that the efficient use of this valuable furnace by-product was considered essential. There, the gas could be used for heating open-hearth steelmaking furnaces, soaking pits, and heat-treating furnaces, or used to generate steam to operate rolling mill engines, drop-forge hammers, and other various and sundry uses. This relatively inefficient use of by-products was simply one of the myriad reasons why changing technologies were to drive many of the merchant pig producers like Lock Ridge out of business.

View of the stockhouse, elevators, Durham stoves, and No. 7 stack. The small frame structure in the lower right corner is the ore-sampling shed. None of the men standing on the stockpile of magnetic ores have been identified. Circa 1910. *Courtesy Alva Beers.*

Furnace crew posing at the entrance to one of the cast houses. The small narrow-gauge engine, the Cinderella, was used to haul pigs from the cast house and slag cars to the dump. Circa 1903. *Courtesy Alva Beers.*

When the original single-chamber pipe stoves were dismantled, they were replaced with four interconnected Durham stoves which provided significantly greater hot blast capacity and far more operating flexibility. While it was somewhat more costly to build four smaller stoves than a single larger one, the smaller stoves could be more easily controlled and more efficiently operated than one large one. The four stoves were manifolded in such a way that any one of the units could be bypassed if a single stove required maintenance or suffered pipe failure. Previously, when only a large, single stove was employed, any pipe failure shut down the whole furnace whereas now the furnace could still be run fairly efficiently on three stoves and possibly even with only two stoves in operation.

Despite the fact that the Durham stoves at Lock Ridge were designed to minimize pipe failure, failures did indeed occur. Those pipes closest to the combustion chamber distorted very readily, although they were not changed until they actually broke. Each of the cast iron "U" pipes weighed between 4200 and 4800 pounds; replacing them was no easy task. The pipe-chamber roof was constructed in such a way that the fire bricks could be removed from their steel or iron supporting members to provide access for the pipe change. A framework was erected to support a pulley (sheave) above the opening from which the pipe was to be removed. A heavy rope or cable was then attached to the top of the pipe, passed through the pulley and connected to the plant locomotive, the Massasoit. After the cast iron sleeve connecting the "U" pipe to the bed pipe was broken with a heavy sledge, the locomotive could pull the damaged pipe from the stove and a replacement pipe could be lowered down.

On numerous occasions during his tenure as president of the Thomas Iron Company, B.F. Fackenthal, Jr. had recommended that no further expense be wasted on the obsolete Lock Ridge facility. However, his successor, Ralph H. Sweetser, had different ideas and during late 1914 and early 1915 two modern McKee-Nelson checker-brick regenerative stoves were added to No. 7 furnace. These stoves, which were 18 feet in diameter and 80 feet high, were constructed directly behind one of the Durham pipe stoves with which they were connected, the pipe stove serving as a preheater. The cylindrical shell was formed from riveted steel plate and the checkerwork inside contained over 200,000 refractory brick. A common stack to provide draft when a stove was "on gas" was located behind the two stoves. The foundations for these stoves can still be seen just to the south of the No. 7 cast house.

In the two-pass McKee-Nelson stove, the furnace gas was burned in the elliptical combustion chamber along one side of the stove.

The superheated air was then drawn through the checkers, which absorbed and retained the heat. After a stove was "on gas" for two hours and the superheated air had soaked nearly to the center of the individual bricks, the stove was put "on blast." This was accomplished by closing the gas valve and opening the cold blast and hot blast valves thereby allowing the blast air, already preheated in the pipe stoves, to pass through the checkers and absorb additional heat from the nearly white-hot refractory brick. The other stove, which was previously "on blast," was then put "on gas" to reheat the checkers. The standard operating procedure at Lock Ridge was to alternate the stoves every two hours. With the addition of these stoves, blast temperatures as high as 1250 degrees could be obtained and a considerable savings in furnace fuel costs realized. Refractory brick could withstand these high temperatures without deterioration and maintenance was much less a problem than with the iron pipe stoves. Today, in advanced designs of the checkerbrick stove, blast temperatures exceeding 2000 degrees are not uncommon.

BOILERS

The original boiler house was located on the masonry structure above the engine room between the two furnace stacks. The boiler plant consisted of ten plain cylindrical boilers, entirely without internal flues, arranged in two rows of five each. Each boiler was 66 inches in diameter by 36 feet long and each had an 18 inch diameter by 18 foot long mud drum beneath it. Each boiler was capable of providing up to 25 pounds of steam, which was sufficient for running the low-pressure blowing engines and other steam engines around the furnace plant; the total capacity of the whole boiler plant was 500 horsepower.

The boilers were heated by furnace gas taken from a flue at the top of each of the stacks. They were exposed directly to the flames of the burning gas up to a height just below the water level in the horizontally mounted cylinder. Each row of five boilers had its own stack to provide the draft required to draw the flames across the bottom of the boiler chamber, the gases making only a single straight pass through to the chimney connection. The draft stack for the row of boilers heated by the gas taken from No. 8 furnace was close to No. 7 furnace; similarly, the fraft stack for No. 7's boiler house was next to No. 8 furnace. Although these cylindrical boilers, were very inefficient because of their limited heating surface and because they allowed the heated air to go up the stack after only a single pass, they served the furnace well for fifty years.

Around 1915 or 1916 a Mr. Biery, a state boiler inspector, condemned the old boiler plant and in 1917 steps were taken to build

69

an entirely new modern facility. The new boiler house was constructed on ground level, between but slightly behind the cast houses. Five modern Babcock and Wilcox water-tube boilers were set up
in the new boiler house and a large draft stack was constructed
nearby. These new boilers were generally fired by furnace gas
conveyed to the combustion chamber by large pipes similar to the
"downcomer." However, during the closing years of the Lock Ridge
operation, both furnaces were seldom in blast concurrently, so there
was sometimes insufficient furnace gas being produced to heat both
the stoves and the boilers. On these occasions soft coal or coke
was burned in the boiler's combustion chamber in order to maintain
adequate steam pressure. The new boilers with their large number
of small-diameter pipes exposed to the flames were far more efficient than the cylindrical boilers they replaced, which accounts for
the fact that only five were needed to generate as much power as
the ten earlier ones. Their chief drawback was that the small-diameter pipes were difficult to clean when impurities in the water were
deposited on their internal surfaces.

BLOWING ENGINES

The blowing engines, which provided the blast for driving the
furnaces, were located in the engine room between the two furnace
stacks. This room was constructed of heavy stone walls similar to
most other early furnace plants. It now houses most of the Lock
Ridge Furnace Museum displays.

The exact configuration of the original blowing engines at Lock
Ridge is not completely known. It is believed that the two original
engines had 32 inch diameter steam cylinders and 60 inch blowing
cylinders. The size of the blowing cylinder is supported somewhat
by Samuel Thomas's statement, quoted earlier, that the five-foot
cylinders were the same ones left on the dock at Cardiff, Wales, and
later used in the construction of the blowing engines installed at
the Crane Iron Works behind Furnace No. 1. One of these original
engines was still in use as a spare until 1918. Two larger blowing
engines of the same style and size as those used at furnaces Nos. 4
and 5 at Hokendauqua were installed sometime late in the nineteenth
century. It is believed that these engines had blowing cylinders 72
inches in diameter with a 72 inch stroke and a steam-cylinder diameter of either 38 or 40 inches.

These early engines were all of the walking-beam, steam- condensing type. The steam cylinder's piston rod was connected to a
gallows beam and thence via a crank to a heavy, large-diameter
flywheel. The blowing cylinder's piston rod was connected to the
other end of the gallows beam and each stroke of the steam cylinder
would provide a corresponding stroke of the blowing cylinder.

Cold-blast pipes were fitted to each end of the vertically positioned blowing cylinder so that air was compressed on both directions of the stroke; the flywheel provided the momentum for the return stroke of the steam cylinder. Air was introduced into the blowing cylinder by a leather flap valve at one end of the cylinder while the air previously introduced was being compressed at the opposite end. (The pieces of leather used in the flap valve were shoe leather, approximately 11 inches by 9 inches, and the worn material was frequently informally requisitioned by employees to make repairs to their personal footwear.) The air that was compressed in this manner was led through a large-diameter pipe, referred to as the cold blast main, to the stoves, where it was heated as described earlier.

During World War I, the Thomas Iron Company purchased two large vertical blowing engines from a firm on Staten Island. These engines, while far more modern than the ones described above, were not new but were surplus engines obtained by brokers from merchant iron companies that had already gone out of business. One of these engines was installed at the furnaces in Hellertown; a little later the other was installed at Lock Ridge. The exact date of its installation is not known. In the stockholders' report made on June 6, 1917, the directors advised that an additional blowing engine had been purchased for Lock Ridge; in their December 31, 1917, report (actually made January 18, 1918) they reported that the engine was being installed; in their December 31, 1918, report, the directors indicated that the engine had been, in fact, installed. According to Milton Knedler, who was blacksmith at Lock Ridge during this period and who had to repair a broken link in the heavy chain used to position the engine, it was finally set in place on Armistice Day, November 11, 1918. He also reports that immediately after it was installed, many of the workers traveled to Macungie where the Macungie Band was playing to celebrate the war's end.

This vertical engine had a steam cylinder 40 inches in diameter on the bottom and a blowing cylinder 96 inches in diameter on the top, both pistons being connected to the same piston rod. The huge flywheel was 24 feet in diameter and the rim was 24 inches square. A ten-inch steam line from the new water-tube boilers was connected to the steam cylinder. This new engine was to see only little more than three years service before it was scrapped along with the rest of the furnace plant.

THE STOCK HOUSES

The three stock houses were constructed on the side of the furnace stack opposite the cast houses. These buildings were two-and-one-half stories high and were built of stone, with slate-covered roofs supported by heavy timber framing members. Ventilators, built over the full length of the peak, were provided with windows to admit light as well as permit ventilation. High stone arches were constructe both on the lower level to provide access between the stock houses, and also between the stock houses and the two elevators.

Raw materials were brought to the stock houses both by wagon and by rail car. Trestles, constructed with heavy wood timbers, were extended into each of the buildings for a distance of approximately 60 feet. Each stock house had two trestles on which standard gauge track was laid for rail deliveries; there was also a roadway between the tracks to accommodate wagon deliveries. Rail cars were weighed at a weighing station some distance down the track near the mainline of the East Penn Division of the Reading Railroad; wagons were weighed on the scale in front of the office. The raw materials, whether iron ore, limestone, or anthracite coal, were unloaded from the cars or wagons and dumped onto piles on the level beneath the trestles. The various types of ore (limonite, magnetite, and later on hematite brought in from the Lakes or overseas) were segregated into separate piles. Occasionally, extra quantities of raw materials were stockpiled in exterior storage areas adjacent to the stock houses.

Sheet-iron, and later steel, filling barrows were loaded with ore, coal, or stone, and wheeled to a Fairbanks-Morse furnace-charging scale installed near the base of each of the elevators. There each was weighed to assure that the correct proportion of the raw materials would be charged. These filling barrows were used almost exclusively for stock charging at all iron furnaces until the early 1890s when the larger iron and steel companies experimented with skip charging techniques and equipment. The larger furnaces being built shortly before the turn of the century required such vast quantities of raw materials that it became impossible for a crew of men using filling barrows and vertical elevators to feed their voracious appetites. The barrows were charged manually at Lock Ridge throughout its entire span of operation.

Because the weight per volume of anthracite coal was roughly comparable to that of the local ores and limestone, a single style of filling barrow was used until around 1915. These superbly balanced barrows had two wheels, with at least one of the wheels loose on its axle to allow for easy cornering in confined areas. They had sturdy legs in the rear so that they could sit level for weighing and standing. The Barrows were dumped by tipping them forward at the axle, the wheels remaining stationary when they were pushed against the dumping ring at the furnace top. A leather-faced wooden pad was sometimes attached to the front of the barrows to cushion the shock when they were dropped with a hard blow onto the dumping ring. These barrows were very heavily constructed to withstand the torturous, continuous use to which they were subjected. The average barrow used at the larger iron furnaces weighed as much as 800 pounds and could carry a load of about 1500 pound of ore. While the smaller barrows used at Lock Ridge had a capacity of only around 500 pounds, it was still a substantial weight to be pushed around by a single man.

After 1915, when beehive and by-product coke were used at Lock Ridge on a regular basis, second-hand filling barrows were purchased, ones that were designed specifically for handling coke. Because of the vast difference in specific gravity between coke, ore and limestone, a much larger barrow could be used to convey the much lighter coke. These larger coke barrows had a top-hinged door at the front, held shut by a latch operated from the back end of the barrow. A moment before dumping, the latch was released by the top-filler. These second-hand coke barrows, as purchased, were too large to fit into the elevator cages and the plant blacksmith, Milton Knedler, had to alter them before they could be put into service.

THE ELEVATORS

As can easily be seen in the photographs accompanying this text, the elevator structures, or hoist houses, were considerably taller than the furnace stacks. They were constructed of timbers and sheathed with vertical planks. The roofs were covered with slate and the ventilating cupolas were ornamental as well as functional. Each hoist house was provided with a flight of stairs to provide access to the furnace top if the elevator was not operating, and windows were installed at each landing. The purpose of the elevators was to transport the filling barrows from the stock-house floor to the charging platform surrounding the furnace mouth. After being weighed, the filling barrows were wheeled into the elevator cage, which accommodated three of the smaller filling barrows that were used exclusively until around 1915. At the top of the elevator the barrows were pushed across the bridge to the charging platform and dumped onto the bell that sealed the furnace top. The material being charged was distributed evenly around the bell so that when the bell was dropped, the burden would form a well-distributed layer inside the stack. The furnace was charged alternately with coal, ore, and limestone, much care being taken to achieve the proper proportion and distribution to maximize efficiency and minimize operating costs.

While vertical elevators were employed at all anthracite furnaces in this area until the 1890s when the Bethlehem Iron Company began installing skip-charging machinery, the manner of operating these elevators varied considerably from one furnace plant to another. The first Lehigh Crane Iron Company elevators were powered by a "water balance," many were operated by steam hoists, but those at Lock Ridge were powered by a large hydraulic cylinder. The 18 foot by 26 foot O.D. cylinder was located in a tunnel under the engine house. The wire rope used to lift the cages was passed over a sheave at the top of the elevator structure and then dropped down, passing through various guides, and attached to heavy rods, 3½ inches in diameter, which were screwed into the head of the piston. Two weights of approximately 4400 pounds each were used as counter balances. The piston was operated by water pressure from a tall water standpipe. This pipe was 132 feet high, towering above the furnace stacks and extending to the level below the engine room; it was 56 inches in diameter at the bottom and tapered to 48 inches at the top. The head of water was maintained at 62 psi, the pressure being monitored on a gauge in front of the blowing engines in the engine room. The hoist guides were 88 feet high, beginning at the base of the stock house and extending above the furnace-charging bridge. The movement of the enclosed platform up and down these guides was controlled by the action of the hydrostatically operated piston.

THE CAST HOUSES

The two Lock Ridge cast houses were identical in construction and appearance. They were solid stone structures with moderately pitched roofs and enough windows to provide adequate interior lighting. Ventilators were constructed along nearly the full length of the peak to dissipate the smoke and heat that escaped during the furnace tap. A doorway, fitted with a sliding wooden door and large enough to allow for passage of the narrow-gauge engines, the Fairy and the Cinderella, was constructed in the wall of each cast house opposite the furnace stack. The size of the cast house was directly proportional to the capacity of the furnace. It had to be large enough so that each side could accommodate all the iron from each furnace tap. While the iron from a previous tap was cooling on one side of the floor to the point where it could be handled, the pig beds were being prepared on the other side for the next cast. By the time this bed was prepared and made ready for the cast, the pigs had been removed from the first side.

The cast house was the very heart of the furnace operation for it was there that the furnace was tapped and the molten iron directed into the pig beds. The tap hole consisted of an opening in the brick hearth lining, located at the base of the hearth, or crucible. It was filled with a sand-and-fireclay plug while the furnace was being blown. Casting, or tapping, was performed at six-hour intervals, or four times a day, seven days a week, as long as the furnace was in blast. Efficient operations could be maintained only by operating the furnace continuously. If the furnace were allowed to cool down to any great extent, the brickwork would contract and probably result in the collapse of the entire lining. In modern blast-furnace practice the furnace is blown at full pressure throughout most of the cast, the pressure being reduced slightly toward the end of the cast when only a small quantity of iron and cinder remain in the crucible. However, in early anthracite iron-making practice, the wind was shut off completely when it was time to cast.

The primary reason for this difference in practice is that in these smaller early furnaces the tuyeres were just a few feet above the tap hole and if the blast remained on, part of the pressure would be directed downwards, driving the iron from the tap hole with great violence. This was especially dangerous when all operations had to be performed by men working in close proximity to the molten metal. In a large modern furnace, the tuyeres are considerably higher and the much larger pool of molten iron cushions the blast. However, when the hearth is nearly completely drained and the blast pressure is felt nearer the tap hole, the action there becomes very violent, necessitating some reduction in wind pressure. Since many of the more dangerous operations are now performed remotely, some short-duration, albeit violent hot-metal splashing at the tap hole can be tolerated.

After the blast was stopped, the plug was knocked out by driving a long rod through the tap hole. When molten iron began to flow, it was directed into the iron, or casting, trough and thence to the pig beds. The slag or cinder was separated from the molten iron by the dam and skimmer. The refractory-brick, sand-covered dam was constructed about eight to ten feet from the tap hole with the skimmer directly above it. As the level of the pool of iron built up behind the dam, the skimmer was raised to allow the iron to flow over the dam and at the same time divert the slag into the cinder trough or runner. This slag trough was built at a level slightly higher than the iron trough and led out a doorway in the side of the cast house into the waiting cinder cars. During the initial phase of the tapping operation the bulk of the material coming through the iron notch was molten iron, with only small quantities of slag floating on top. As the crucible was emptied, more and more slag came through. When the flow slowed down and nearly all the iron was out, the tap hole was closed again by ramming a new sand-and-fireclay plug into the tap hole.

In modern furnaces the tapping and plugging operations are performed remotely. A hydraulically positioned drill is used to bore through the tap hole and a pneumatic mud gun is used to plug it up again. Both operations are controlled from a glass-enclosed, air-conditioned room located well above the cast floor and many feet distant from the iron notch; there is virtually no hazard to the operator. At Lock Ridge, and all other furnaces of its period, these activities were performed manually, the caster working in close proximity to the molten iron and slag. The heat, especially during the summer, could become almost unbearable, and one false step could result in serious injury, even death.

The cast-house floor was arranged so that the molten iron was conveyed by gravity flow. The iron trough, which carried the molten metal to the sows, was slightly higher than the sows, the sows slightly higher than the pigs. The sows and pigs were so named because of their resemblance to a row of suckling piglets. The sand used for the pig-bed runners had to be coarse and open-grained, and free from clay, lime, iron oxide, and other impurities. It was moistened to form the pig bed before each cast, but it had to be dried out by casting time. If the sand were too fine or compact, or if any moisture were present, the gases generated by the action of the intense heat of the iron on the water could not escape and a violent bubbling action, almost volcanic in appearance, could occur. Once started, this action could progress to point of near disaster. As the sand was disturbed by these ebullitions, the hot iron was given access to wetter and fresher sand underneath, with the consequent generation of more gas and still more violence. If the iron flow were allowed to continue, this action could progress until a hole many feet deep was eaten into the cast-house floor and the problem of removing the large chunk of iron that filled the cavity was tremendous. If lime, clay, iron oxide, or any other material that could unite with silica at the high temperature of the iron, were present, slag was formed and the dirty iron that resulted was not readily marketable.

The sows and pigs were broken apart after the iron had cooled to a temperature immediately below solidification, but before it had acquired significant strength. First a thin layer of sand was thrown over the still-hot iron. The iron breakers wore clogs with wooden soles about an inch thick, kept soaking in water when not in use, which they strapped to their shoes. The pigs were broken from the sow by applying a crow bar at the junction of the two and lifting with a jerk to snap the pig free. If the iron had cooled too much, a heavy sledge was employed to assist in the process. The sow was allowed to cool a little more and was broken into manageable pieces with the sledge. The size and weight of the pigs have changed little from the early charcoal era to the present, the weight averaging between 85 and 95 pounds, which is about what the average man can handle continuously. Sometimes in the summer, when the heat and humidity made this task barely tolerable, the iron was allowed to cool further, the beds sprinkled with water, and the iron broken cold. While it required considerably more effort to break it cold, this practice probably saved many of the workers from heat exhaustion.

After breaking, the pigs were loaded onto small narrow- gauge cars which ran on a track laid into the end of the cast house. The Fairy and the Cinderella were used to haul these cars to a small pig storage area for later transfer to standard-gauge cars for shipment to foundries, steel furnaces, and rolling mills.

In addition to the major furnace structures already described, the Lock Ridge complex contained a number of ancillary buildings and facilities. These included a blacksmith shop, carpenter shop, machine shop, locomotive barn and shop, ore sampling shed, and office. These facilities were not as extensive and complete at Lock Ridge as at the main Hokendauqua plant, but they were adequate for handling routine requirements and emergency repairs. The blacksmith shop was the building closest to the No. 7 cast house; the carpenter shop was just to the south of the blacksmith shop. Both structures were built of stone and their walls have been partially reconstructed on their original foundations by Lehigh County as part of the Lock Ridge Furnace Museum Park.

The wooden patterns for preparing the pig beds and the clogs used by the iron breakers were among the many items produced in the carpenter shop. The blacksmith shop was primarily a maintenance shop for repairing tools and equipment used around the furnace plant, and it included a small forge for this purpose. The ore-sampling shed was a diminutive frame building used to test incoming ore for iron content and percentage of silicon, phosphorous, and other impurities. The brick office where all the furnace records were maintained, including raw-material inventories and production data, stood along the entrance road to the furnace site. It has been restored to its former appearance and condition. The machine shop was a small brick structure opposite the office. Like the blacksmith shop, it was used primarily for maintenance purposes. The locomotive barn used for housing and maintaining the plant's three steam locomotives was located at the southernmost limits of the furnace plant.

It is not known if the Fairy and the Cinderella were purchased exclusively for Lock Ridge or if they were first used at Hokendauqua and later transferred to Lock Ridge after standard-gauge locomotives replaced the narrow-gauge ones at the Hokendauqua

The Massasoit, manufactured by Baldwin Locomotive Works, on the main line of the Catasauqua and Fogelsville Railroad, beneath the bridge next to the plant's office. Standing on the engine are the engineer, Chester Beers, and the fireman, James Rothenberger. Alongside the locomotive are: Robert McKeever, master mechanic and chief engineer; Michael Kelly; "Happy" Hertzog; Daniel Davis, superintendent; Henry Beers, clerk; C. Unbescheiden, clerk; George Seip, blacksmith; Charles Welty; Joel Adams; S. Marsteller, carpenter. Circa 1903. *Courtesy Alva Beers.*

Daniel Davis and his family in front of the superintendent's house on Franklin Street in Lock Ridge. *Published in the 1904 stockholders report.*

plant in the early 1890s. The following article which appeared in the September 3, 1870, issue of the The Railroad Gazette describes the appearance and purpose of these small locomotives:

Messr's M. Baird & Co., of the Baldwin Locomotive Works, Philadelphia, have built during the present year a number of small locomotives for use in mines, hauling away cinder, etc. The engines referred to are miniature locomotives, adapted to narrow gauges of 2½, 3, or 3½ feet. The Thomas Iron Works, Hokendauqua, the Lehigh Crane Iron Works, Catasauqua, and the Glendon Iron Works, Easton, are each now working two of these machines for hauling away cinder from their furnaces. At the former establishment the two engines do the work which formerly required thirty mules. The economy of their use is therefore manifest. For out of door work the little engines are built with outside cylinders 9 inches in diameter and 12 inches stroke; the driving wheels are 30 inches in diameter . . . These engines, in complete working order, with tank of water on boiler and a man on footboard, will weigh only from six to eight gross tons.

The Massasoit was a full-size, standard-gauge locomotive used for moving ore and coal cars into position in the stockyard area. It was also employed to carry pig-laden cars to the siding along the East Penn Division tracks for transfer to Philadelphia and Reading Railway trains for shipment to the customer. Occasionally trips were made as far as Hokendauqua or Catasauqua over Catasauqua and Fogelsville Railroad tracks.

RAW MATERIALS

The primary furnace fuel at Lock Ridge was anthracite coal, but as early at the mid 1870s some small quantities of coke were intermixed with the charge. In 1914 it was reported that Lock Ridge was the last furnace in the country to rely exclusively on anthracite coal. Soon after this, bee-hive and by-product coke, brought in by rail from western Pennsylvania and West Virginia, became the predominant fuel until the plant shut down.

The ores used were primarily local limonite mixed with lesser quantities of magnetite mined at Rittenhouse Gap or shipped in from the Thomas Iron Company's Richard Mine in Morris County, N.J., 2½ miles north of Dover. The proportions charged generally ranged from 2/3 or 3/4 limonite to 1/3 or 1/4 magnetite. By the mid-1890s Lake ores began to replace limonite as the primary burden. During the administration of Ralph H. Sweetser, efforts were made to cut costs by re-opening some of the local limonite mines. This attempt, made during 1914 through 1917, was largely unsuccessful both because of high startup costs and because inadequate quantities were obtained. By the end of World War I, these efforts had been abandoned and the company was again forced to rely upon Lake and foreign ores.

Most of the limestone used at Lock Ridge came from two nearby quarries, Spring Creek Quarry and Schmoyer's Quarry. Both lay close to the Catasauqua and Fogelsville Railroad. Since this limestone was highly dolomitic, containing nearly as much magnesium as calcium, larger quantities had to be used to achieve the proper fluxing action than in those furnaces using high calcium stone. Because larger quantities of stone had to be quarried, hauled, and charged, and larger quantities of cinder hauled to the dump, operating costs were higher. After 1915, the company stopped using this local stone and purchased high calcium limestone shipped in by rail from Annville, Pennsylvania. The Schmoyer quarry continued to be operated until relatively recently by a number of concerns, the stone being used primarily for highway construction.

THE LOCK RIDGE COMMUNITY

In many respects, life in the Lock Ridge community resembled that of earlier iron plantations. Like the iron- master's home in plantation days, the furnace superintendent's home was one of the largest and most gracious in the community. As on the plantations, tenement housing was provided for many of the company employees. There were 13 double units on Franklin and Thomas streets and two four-family structures on Church Street. While unpretentious, these sturdy brick homes were certainly as comfortable as any the average working man of the late nineteenth century was able to afford. All have now survived for more than a hundred years and many have been modernized by their present owners. While the furnace was in operation, these houses were maintained by the company and were well cared for by the tenants. Nearly all had brightly whitewashed paling fences around them to protect the neatly kept kitchen gardens in the backyard. These paling fences were once a ubiquitous feature throughout the Valley and the annual or semi-annual white-washing task was generally assigned to the older children of the household. In addition to the family houses, the company also maintained a boarding house for unmarried male employees along the southern periphery of the furnace site.

Water for furnace operations was drawn from the Swabia Creek, supplemented by two wells at the furnace site. Drinking water was obtained from a large spring near the Catasauqua and Fogelsville Railroad right-of-way west of Reservoir Road. This spring had a large concrete-lined and- covered collection basin and was fitted with a valve to control the flow. The water was conveyed down the mountainside in iron pipes to hydrants along the roads in front of the company houses. Although the residents had to go outdoors to fetch it, this pure spring water was much preferred to that obtained from local wells. Wellwater was often contaminated by cesspools because of the cavernous limestone underlying the Valley.

The rural location of this furnace plant provided a far more tranquil atmosphere than at the larger furnaces near Allentown and the burgeoning steel mills in cities like Bethlehem and Pittsburgh. There was no major influx of immigrants; therefore the social discord experienced in the larger mill towns was avoided. The work force, which averaged from 85 to 90 men when both furnaces were operating and 44 to 48 men when only one was operating, was composed primarily of long-time area residents of Pennsylvania-German origin along with some Scots, Irish, Scotch-Irish, and a few Welshmen.

The Thomas Iron Company, at least during those years when the Thomas family played an active role in its management, was a benevolent, even paternalistic, employer. Its managers cared for the welfare of their workers and in turn earned their respect. The company took pride in the fact that its personnel policies and practices engendered employee loyalty. When it published its fiftieth-anniversary stockholders report in 1904, it listed all long-term employees and their years of service. This list included many who worked at Lock Ridge, among whom were C. Unbescheiden, clerk, 25 years; H.U. Beers, clerk, 22 years; Chester Beers, locomotive engineer and later clerk, 39 years; Robert McKeever, chief engineer and master mechanic, 39 years; Francis Boger, 36 years; Sylvester J. Lehrman, engineer, 33 years; James Rothenberger, locomotive fireman, 32 years; Henry Knerr, foreman and later superintendent, 33 years; Joel Adams, 27 years; Sylvester Kemmerer, 26 years; Henry Beers, 25 years; Albert Herbert, 25 years; George Seip, blacksmith, 25 years. Many of the employees continued to work for the company for many more years, until their death or until the furnace shut down.

SUPERINTENDENTS

The men who served as superintendents at Lock Ridge were generally possessed of considerable talent and experience and were a credit to the iron industry. A brief biographical sketch of each, in order of their service, follows:

Valentine Weygandt Weaver, superintendent from 1866 to August 1, 1873. V.W. Weaver was born on January 9, 1826, the eldest son of Charles Weaver and Catherine B. (Hummel) Weaver. During his teens, V.W. Weaver worked for a few years as a store clerk in a number of communities in the area then, at the age of 20 years, he became machinist's apprentice at the Crane Iron Company at Catasauqua. In

1848 he married Mary Mickley, daughter of Jacob Mickley of White-hall Township. In March of the same year Mary's sister, Rebecca, was married to Samuel Thomas. After working as a machinist and mining agent for a few years, V.W. Weaver left the Crane Iron Company to become assistant superintendent at the Thomas Iron Company at Hokendauqua, working under his brother-in-law Samuel Thomas, who was then acting as superintendent. When Samuel Thomas was advanced to president in 1864, Weaver succeeded him as superintendent. He had served in this position for only a few years when he was called upon to supervise the construction of the Lock Ridge furnace and become its first superintendent. In August, 1873, V.W. Weaver left Lock Ridge and for a while managed the company's iron mines at Pine Grove for the South Mountain Iron Company. He then left the employ of the Thomas Iron Company and became superintendent of the Millerstown Iron Company near Macungie. He later left the bankrupt furnace at Macungie and in July, 1879, became superintendent of the Coplay Iron Company where he remained for a few years. He served as a director of the Macungie Iron Company, the Hokendauqua Bridge Company, and the national banks of Catasauqua and Slatington. He died in Catasauqua on October 11, 1893. V.W. Weaver's son, James W. Weaver, brother of William M. (see below), also served the Thomas Iron Company for many years, beginning in 1867 as a machinist at Hokendauqua and then as clerk and telegraph operator at Lock Ridge. He was then at Pine Grove for six years and the Coplay Iron Company for three years. On June 25, 1883 he was re-employed by the Thomas Iron Company as bookkeeper in the eastern office, a position he held until February 9, 1893 when he was promoted to secretary. On February 9, 1893, he also became treasurer and served the company in this dual capacity until 1915.

William Mickley Weaver, superintendent from October 16, 1873, to April 7, 1877. William M. Weaver was born July 18, 1851, in Catasauqua, the son of Valentine Weygandt Weaver and Mary (Mickley) Weaver. He received his early education in local schools and at Williamsport; then, at the age of 18 or 19 he entered the Baldwin Locomotive Works in Philadelphia to study mechanics and remained there for three years. In 1873, he assumed the superintendency of the Lock Ridge Furnaces, succeeding his father. He was then only 22, making him the youngest furnace superintendent in Pennsylvania up until that time. After less than four years at Lock Ridge, he moved to Macungie to succeed his father as superintendent until his tragically early death on March 19, 1890 at the age of 38.

Edwin Thomas, superintendent from April 7, 1877, to April 1, 1880. Edwin Thomas was born in Catasauqua on April 9, 1853, the son of Samuel Thomas and Rebecca (Mickley) Thomas. He attended local schools in Catasauqua, college preparatory school in Swarthmore, and subsequently Lafayette College. He then worked for three years as a machinist at the Hokendauqua plant of the Thomas Iron Company after which he was transferred to serve as superintendent of the furnaces of the Chestnut Hill Iron Ore Company at Columbia, Pennsylvania, remaining there for two years. He then returned to the Hokendauqua plant and served for four years as purchasing agent and manager of the mechanical department. In 1886 Edwin accompanied his father to Alabama to assist in designing and erecting the furnace plant of the Pioneer Mining and Manufacturing Company, of which he became vice-president. In 1892 he succeeded his father as president, a position he held until the Thomases sold the plant at Thomas, Alabama, to the Republic Iron and Steel Company in 1899. He served as manager for the new owners for one year, after which he resigned and returned to Catasauqua. He served as president of the Catasauqua National Bank and the Nescopee Coal Company, and was a director of the Upper Lehigh Coal Company, the Wahnetah Silk Company, the Thomas Iron Company, and various other industrial enterprises. Edwin Thomas last served as an officer of the Thomas Iron Company during 1915 and 1916, when he held the position of vice-president for a brief period.

David H. Thomas, superintendent from April 1, 1880, to March 1, 1885. David H. Thomas was born in Catasauqua on December 18, 1860, the son of John and Helen (Thomas) Thomas. He entered the machine shop at the Hokendauqua plant on June 21, 1875, and on April 1, 1880, he was appointed to succeed his cousin as superintendent of Lock Ridge. He was then nineteen. While at Lock Ridge he supervised the modifications to the furnaces described earlier. He resigned this position on March 1, 1885, to manage a furnace plant in Alabama. He remained in Alabama just a short time, leaving to become superintendent of the Troy Steel and Iron Company's furnaces at Breaker Island, N.Y., where he supervised the construction of three new blast furnaces. On April 1, 1888, he was re-employed by the Thomas Iron Company, and served as superintendent of the Hokendauqua plant until March 1, 1893, when he succeeded his father as general superintendent, a position he held for many years.

Daniel Davis, superintendent from March 1, 1885, to October 15, 1907. Daniel Davis, son of Noah and Margaret (Gwynne) Davis, was born in Hazelton, Pennsylvania, on March 12, 1842. His parents moved to Catasauqua when he was three years of age. After attending school there, he began working at the blacksmith shop of the Crane Iron Company. He enlisted at age 18, and compiled a distinguished combat record during the Civil War. After the war he served as the first agent of the Central Railroad of New Jersey at Catasauqua, a position he held until November 5, 1879, when he received the position of superintendent of the Keystone Furnace at Island Park.

When the Thomas Iron Company acquired the Keystone Furnace in 1882, Davis remained there as superintendent until March 1, 1885, when he was transferred to Lock Ridge. He served as superintendent at Lock Ridge for over 22 years, longer than any before or after him. He was considered an able manager, respected by his employees, and active in affairs of the communities of Lock Ridge and Alburtis. After leaving Lock Ridge he returned to Catasauqua where he lived the remainder of his life.

John W. Thomas, superintendent from October 15, 1907, to June 1912. John W. Thomas, third son of John and Helen (Thomas) Thomas was employed during his early years by the Crane Iron Company. He left his position as manager of those furnaces on December 1, 1900, to become manager of the Hokendauqua furnaces of the Thomas Iron Company. On March 9, 1903, he was appointed superintendent of the Keystone Plant at Island Park where he remained until 1907 when he was transferred to Lock Ridge.

Henry Knerr, superintendent from July 1912 to his death on March 7, 1920. Henry Knerr was born on Sept. 11, 1856, in Upper Macungie Township, the son of David and Mary (Smith) Knerr. He was educated in the public schools and from the age of eight years worked on the farm. Later he was employed in a stone quarry and for a period of two years hauled iron ore. In 1875 he began his 45-year employment with the Thomas Iron Company at Lock Ridge, starting as a laborer and progressing through numerous jobs until he became foreman. He held the position of foreman for 24 years until 1912, when he was promoted to superintendent. A number of his descendants still live in Alburtis and Macungie.

The last iron made at Lock Ridge was smelted in No. 7 Furnace during November and December of 1921. Only 2,061 tons were produced. The last stockholders report of the Thomas Iron Company, presented on February 1, 1922, by the company's last president, W.A. Barrow, noted that the Hokendauqua plant had been out of blast since February 4, 1921, and the Hellertown plant had produced only 6,142 tons during the last two months of 1921. Neither the Lock Ridge nor the Hellertown furnaces were ever reactivated.

The Lock Ridge plant was sold to the William Butz family of Alburtis for its scrap value. The buildings were largely dismantled over the span of a few years; ferrous metals that could be retrieved were hauled away for sale, wooden structures were pulled down to be re-used in the construction of new buildings or burned in cookstoves. However, the masonry structures were never completely demolished and enough of the ruins remained that a later generation of the Butz family was able to offer the site to Lehigh County to be resurrected as a park and museum commemorating the county's leading industry of the nineteenth century.

Lehigh Slag Company plant, built in 1922 and operated until 1958. It provided much coarse slag for the sub-base of the Northeast Extension of the Pennsylvania Turnpike between Emmaus and the Blue Mountain tunnel. *Courtesy Clinton Hillegass.*

LEHIGH SLAG COMPANY

After ironmaking operations ceased in 1921, the slag dumps at Lock Ridge were leased to the Lehigh Slag Company. The principal owner and president of this company was Herman A. Kostenbader, one of the owners of the Eagle Brewery in Catasauqua. Kostenbader had earlier operated a slag processing business at the Thomas Iron company's dumps at Hokendauqua.

Two steam-driven Marion shovels dug the slag from the dumps and loaded it into small side-dump cars. A Vulcan locomotive pulled the cars to a spot above the crusher, where the load was dumped down a chute into the primary crusher. After the slag passed through a series of crushers a bucket elevator carried it to the top of the screening building, where it was graded into various sizes then loaded into trucks or hopper cars for shipment to customers.

The original primary crusher was manufactured by the Traylor Engineering Company of Allentown. It was replaced by a Buchanan jaw crusher made by the Birdsboro Corporation of Birdsboro, Pennsylvania. After passing through the primary crusher, the slag was generally processed through three additional crushers, first through a Traylor gyratory crusher, then through a New Holland roll crusher (made in New Holland, Pennsylvania), and finally through a roll crusher manufactured by the Fuller Company of Catasauqua.

Immediately before it was screened, the crushed material went through a Cutler Hammer magnetic separator, which recovered significant amounts of iron. This was sold to a broker, who sold it to the Brooke Iron Company to be remelted in their Birdsboro plant.

The screening house contained a Kennedy Van Saun double-decker screen and a rotary screen for separating the crushed slag into the various commercial grades. Most of the processed slag was used for highway construction and for built-up roofs. While some of the finer roofing slag was shipped as far away as New England, much of it was consumed by roofing companies in the immediate area. The Lehigh Slag Company provided 135,000 tons of coarse (1 to 4 inch screen) slag for the sub-base of the Northeast Extension of the Pennsylvania Turnpike from Emmaus to the Blue Mountain tunnel. Operations ended in 1958, and the buildings of the slag plant were burned down under the supervision of general manager Clinton Hillegass.

CHAPTER IV

IRON MINING AND MINERAL RESOURCES

The Lehigh Valley of the nineteenth century had abundant reserves of iron ore and other resources used by its nascent industries. Before the days of environmental protection agencies, these
materials were there for the taking with little or no concern for
the impact of quarrying and mining on streams, farmland, or inhabitants. Iron ores, limestone, slate, and "cement rock" were taken
from the ground to be converted into marketable commodities. The
scars remain, as do the descendants of many of the immigrants who
came to the Valley to find work.

While some mines were opened in the Lehigh Valley region to
provide ore to nearby charcoal furnaces, it was not until the development of anthracite technology and the concomitant demand for
vastly increased quantities of raw materials that this natural resource was exploited in earnest. Brown hematite ores, called limonite in modern terminology, were mined early in the nineteenth
century and carted to the few charcoal furnaces scattered throughout the region. During the explosive growth of the anthracite iron
industry after the year 1840, the search for ore was to change the
landscape of the Valley, and of Lehigh County in particular.

During the 1840s, numerous mines were opened in the Valley.
Ore was hauled in wagons over dirt tracks to the new furnaces
along the Lehigh river. By the 1850s, as many people were employed
mining ore as were tending the furnaces. A contemporary account by
Macungie attorney E.R. Lichtenwallner, describing activities in Lower
Macungie Township, appeared in Mathews and Hungerford's 1884 History of Lehigh and Carbon Counties:

> Within a few years previous to the "financial crash" of
> 1874 some very rich and valuable deposits of hematite iron-
> ore were uncovered in this township, and it seemed at one
> time as if almost everybody who owned a tract of land, how-
> ever small, had been seized with the mining fever. Leases
> were made, shafts sunk, and the "hidden treasure" sought for
> everywhere. Ore-washeries and smoke-stacks seemed to
> spring up throughout the township like mushrooms in a hot-
> bed, while the fires from the chimneys of two furnaces and
> a foundry, erected within the confines of the township, lit
> up the night with their lurid flames. Although many beauti-
> ful farms were laid waste, the owners thereof reaped a rich

harvest in the shape of royalties, and considered themselves amply compensated for the unsightly gaps made in their land in consequence of mining the ore. That section of the township know as "the Flats" situate near East Texas was singularly productive in this respect, and as the ore was mainly what is termed "top-ore", the land in that vicinity was soon reduced to a barren waste, as it now remains. On account of the depressed condition of the iron trade in 1874 many of the mines, however, were stopped, owing to the low price offered for ore, and today comparatively few of them are to be seen in operation.

Other sources corroborate Lichtenwallner's comments on the extent of the mining fever. J.P. Lesley, in his Iron Manufacturer's Guide, reported scores of active mines throughout the Lehigh Valley in 1856. The Second Pennsylvania Geological Survey, conducted in the Lehigh Valley by Lafayette College professor Frederick Prime, Jr. and associates between 1874 and 1884, described 261 limonite mines in Lehigh County and 84 in Northampton County. While only a few dozen were opened in the last two decades of the century, operations at some of the large and more productive mines were continued through World War I.

The Lehigh Valley is but a small part of the Great Valley which, although not well defined throughout its length, extends in a southwesterly direction from New England to Alabama. In eastern Pennsylvania, this valley is bordered on the northwest by the Kittatinny Ridge or Blue Mountain and on the southwest by the South Mountains. The Kittatinny Ridge is composed principally of Silurian sandstones and conglomerates. The South Mountains are complex crystalline structures of pre-Cambrian igneous origin. In eastern Pennsylvania and New Jersey these hills, often referred to as the Reading Prong, have been metamorphosed into gneisses. In many locations these hills contained huge deposits of magnetic ores, the largest of these being the Morris County mines in New Jersey and the Cornwall Mines in southern Lebanon County. At both of these locations deposits were first opened during the Colonial era for charcoal furnaces and have been worked into the 1970s.

In the Lehigh Valley region the Durham Mines were opened in 1727 and worked sporadically until the early twentieth century. At various locations between Emmaus and Vera Cruz in Lehigh County, also at Siesholtzville and Rittenhouse Gap in Berks County, mines opened in the early anthracite era were operated until the early years of the twentieth century.

Since the magnetic ores outcropped at the surface, early mining techniques were similar to quarrying operations. By the middle of the nineteenth century the surface ores were largely expended and a number of deep-mining techniques had been introduced. Experienced tin miners from Cornwall, England, and coal miners from Wales were encouraged to emigrate and settle in these areas because of their knowledge of deep mining. During the twentieth century, ore was being extracted from depths of more than 1,000 feet at Mount Hope, New Jersey, and well over 2,000 feet at Cornwall. At Cornwall, open-pit mining was carried on concurrently with deep mining until 1972. At the Bethlehem Steel Corporation's Grace Mine near Morgantown, Pennsylvania, which was opened in 1955, ore was being extracted from levels as deep as 4,500 feet when the operation was shut down on October 31, 1977, because of the company's diminishing need for ore.

The floor of the Great Valley is underlain principally by Cambrian and Ordovician limestones in the south, and Ordovician shales in the north. Some of these shales of the Martinsburg formation have been metamorphosed into slate, which outcrops in a band that extends from Slatedale in Lehigh County to Portland on the Delaware River. Slate-quarrying operations, begun during the second quarter of the nineteenth century, remained commercially important until the 1950s, when the introduction of cheaper substitutes caused a rapid decline in the demand for roofing slates and school blackboards. Today only a few quarries remain in operation, producing replacement roofing slates and pool-table slabs.

The limestone formations of the Great Valley vary considerably in their chemical composition. At some locations, such as Annville in Lebanon county, Hanover in York County, and near McAfee in northwestern New Jersey, deposits occur that are very high in calcium carbonate. These locations have provided stone for blast-furnace and open-hearth flux for many years. At Annville and Hanover, limekilns also produce the "pebble lime" used in Bethlehem Steel's basic oxygen furnaces in Bethlehem and at Sparrows Point, Maryland.

The limestones of Lehigh and Northampton counties are highly dolomitic, often containing nearly as much magnesium as calcium. Even though this makes them of inferior quality for metallurgical fluxing purposes, they were used for furnace flux during the anthracite era because of their proximity to the furnace plants. By the early twentieth century, however, those iron producers who were still operating began to import high-calcium limestone from Lebanon County and New Jersey.

The Jacksonburg limestone, an Ordovician formation that occurs along the edge of the Martinsburg shales, is at the same time the most impure and the most commercially valuable limestone in the Lehigh Valley. Its very impurity makes it highly prized for the manufacture of cement. This "cement rock" was first used for the production of hydraulic, or natural, cement to build many of the locks on the Lehigh Canal. By the early 1870s, Davis O. Saylor was using it to manufacture the first portland cement produced in the United States.

As the iron industry was declining during the late nineteenth century, the cement industry was rapidly increasing in importance. Just as entrepreneurs had rushed in the mid-nineteenth century to take advantage of the technology that used anthracite to make iron, so some thirty years later they invested heavily in Saylor's discovery and dozens of cement plants were built along the Jacksonburg formation from Fogelsville in western Lehigh County to Warren County, New Jersey, in the east.

For many years, Lehigh Valley mills manufactured more than half of the portland cement produced in the United States. Virtually all the concrete used in the construction of the Panama Canal was made with portland cement from the Lehigh Valley. Although most of the older, smaller plants have been shut down in recent years, and the modern plants that remain are all owned by European firms, the Lehigh District continues to be one of the most important producers of cement in the nation.

The limonite or brown hematite ores that were used so extensively during the anthracite era are essentially identical to the bog ores used in the earliest Colonial furnaces, such as the Saugus Furnace in Massachusetts and the Pine Barren furnaces in southern New Jersey. These ores are abundant throughout the length of the Great Valley, but were extracted only near those locations where an iron industry developed. In other words, the presence of limonite was never the sole reason for the establishment of a local iron industry. All the other prerequisites for the making of iron had to be available -- fuel, flux, technical ability, and capital.

Limonite's chemical makeup and relatively small percentage of iron, most often 35 to 40 percent, seldom justified its shipment to a distant furnace. On the other hand magnetite, which often contained 55 to 60 percent iron and was more easily and cheaply reduced, was frequently shipped for hundreds of miles when economical means of transportation, such as canal or railroad, could be used. Limonite ores never made such journeys. However, during the anthracite era these brown hematite ores were very extensively mined in Northampton, Lehigh, Berks, Lebanon, Dauphin, York, Cumberland, and Adams counties to supply the local furnaces.

In the Lehigh Valley, the limonite ores are found chiefly above the extensive limestone formations throughout the full length of the Valley proper and also in the Saucon Valley, which is a prominent extension of the Lehigh Valley south of the South Mountains. Many very productive mines were also developed above the Hardyston sandstone structure. The Hardyston, which in many places has been metamorphosed into quartzite, chert, and jasper, occurs near the base of the northern slope of the South Mountain in Lehigh County, and in the high valleys of Williams Township and eastern Lower Saucon Township in Northampton County. Those ores associated with the limestones were referred to locally as "valley ores" and those that occurred with the Hardyston were called "mountain ores." Chemically, they were essentially the same.

The limonite ores were found in several different physical forms, all of which were given descriptive names by the miners. The most common were bombshell or pot ore, pipe ore, and wash ore. The bombshell ore consists of more or less spherical masses of limonite ranging in size from one inch to two feet in diameter. Many of these nodules are hollow. Some are filled with water, others with white or drab clay or fine white or pinkish sand. The walls of the bombshells range in thickness from a fraction of an inch to 1½ inches, and most nodules contain several inner layers that are fibrous in appearance, with clay or water often taking up the voids between the layers of ore. Small stalactites sometimes even occur on the inner walls of the geodes. A lustrous black botryoidal surface, often markedly iridescent, is found in the interior of some of the geodes. The dark color of the interior suggests the presence of considerable quantities of manganese; analyses commonly show this mineral to be present, the percentage being somewhat greater in the mountain ores than in the valley ores. Generally, the bombshell ore is the highest grade found in the Valley and the adhering clay is easily washed from its relatively smooth surface.

Closely related to the bombshell ore are the large, irregular masses of cellular material that represent the bulk of the limonite ores. These masses range from a few inches to more than ten feet in diameter and consist of a network of thin partitions of limonite running in all directions. The cavities, which are usually small and seldom more than a few inches long, are exceedingly irregular in shape and most commonly filled with ocherous clay. The walls of the cavities are coated with a firmly cemented layer of ocher. The comparatively fragile character of this ore allows it to be easily broken into manageable pieces by the miners' picks and sledges.

The type of ore commonly referred to as pipe ore consists of tubes of limonite containing varying quantities of sand. Sometimes large tubes a foot or so in diameter were found, although in most cases they were only one to two inches in diameter. Pieces of pipe ore may originally have been several feet in length, but as they were invariably broken it was unusual to find pieces more than eight inches long. Pipe ore was very common and was the principle ore mined at some locations.

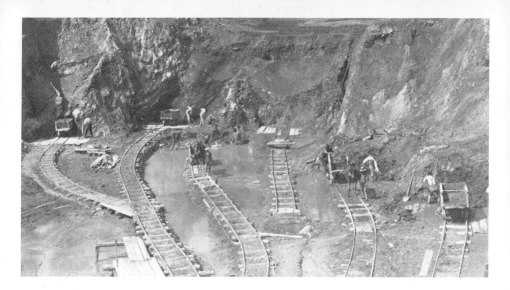

The Koch mine in Lower Saucon Township near Hellertown, Northampton County, was typical of open-pit brown hematite mines in the Lehigh Valley. It was extensively worked first by the Saucon Iron Company and later by the Thomas Iron Company. The ore was primarily wash ore and averaged only 32 percent iron. It was high in phosphorus (.927 percent) but contained 2.48 percent manganese, which was typical of ores underlain by the Hardystone quartzite. Short drifts followed veins of richer ore into the face of the pit. *From the 1904 stockholders report of the Thomas Iron Company.*

Washery plant at the Koch mine. Steam, generated by the boiler plant inside the building next to the draft stack, operated the tramway hoist, the sump pump, and the log washer. At the head of the washer is the gravel picker's shack with a pile of discarded material underneath. Wooden sluiceways carry off the dirty washery water to settling basins. The ore-loading bins are directly behind the gravel picker's shack. *From the 1904 stockholders report of the Thomas Iron Company.*

Wash ore consists of fragments of limonite in the form of irregular particles or plates representing broken pieces of the types of ore already described. This material was invariably present in large quantities., and in many mines it was the only form of ore to be found. The larger pieces of this fragmented ore were recovered in the washer, but many of the finer particles passed through the washer blades and ended up on the dumps.

The origin of these local limonite ores is a very complex geological phenomenon and the processes of their formation have been the subject of controversy among geologists for many years. The original source of the ores is believed to have been the pyrites, magnetites or some ferro-magnesium silicates that were present in the igneous rocks which underlie all the sedimentary strata in which the bodies of ore now occur. Eons ago, when the Appalachian Sea covered this region, the iron found in the igneous strata was first dissolved and then precipitated from solution in the form of pyrite and siderite to form part of the Cambrian and Ordovician sandstones, limestones, and shales that were deposited in its shallow waters. The iron thus deposited in these newer sedimentary strata is, in most cases, believed to have undergone both primary and secondary segregation during its transformation into its present form. The primary segregation of the Valley ores is believed to have been caused by artesian waters forcing the iron in solution upwards through the strata along faults and fracture zones. As the dissolved iron approached the surface, the resultant decrease in temperature and relief of pressure caused the pyrite to precipitate from these ascending waters. The fact that many of the Valley limonite mines are underlain by considerable deposits of pyrite lends some credence to this conclusion.

The secondary concentration of the iron into workable deposits was caused by descending waters carrying oxygen and carbon dioxide in solution, which transformed the original segregations of pyrite either into siderite or directly into limonite. Since siderite is unstable in the presence of highly oxygenated surface water, it has nearly all been changed to limonite near the surface. Considerable quantities may probably still be found in many of the mines, a short distance below the ground-water level.

While the theory of both a primary and a secondary segregation of these local ores, via first ascending then descending waters, may provide a satisfactory explanation for most of the deposits, there are indications that some limonite deposits were the result of the precipitation from descending waters alone. The basis for this conclusion is that in some areas there is no evidence of pyrite ever having been present and there are no deep fissures in the limestone through which ascending waters might have conveyed the pyrite, had it been present. In these areas the deposition of the limonite was probably produced by percolating waters dissolving the disseminated iron minerals that were present in the overlying strata and carrying them as sulfates or bicarbonates until they were checked in their downward movement by impervious shaly strata or saturated strata. The water then gradually precipitated the iron in the form of limonite or carbonate, probably by coming in contact with other surface waters carrying oxygen in solution. The final form of the ores, whether pipe or bombshell, was determined by a variety of rather complex local conditions. The clay that is associated with the limonite ores represents the residual materials left by the decomposition of aluminous and siliceous strata and was formed at the same time that the secondary concentration of the ore occurred.

The limestone floor of the Valley is very irregular, in some places outcropping on the surface, but in most places it lies at a depth ranging from twenty-five feet to more than one hundred feet, probably averaging from thirty-five to sixty-five feet. Generally, more ore was concentrated in those areas where the limestone had disintegrated to the greatest depth as the ground waters flowing downwards through the faults and fissures in the limestone strata, and thereby causing its disintegration, also segregated the ores.

Most of the limonite ores lay relatively close to the surface and were mined principally by the open-cut or open-pit method. This method proved quite satisfactory during the early stages of operation but as some of the richer deposits were mined to considerable depths, the loose overburden tended to slide into the pits after heavy rains. Therefore, mine operators sometimes resorted to shaft mining, sinking shafts in or near the old pits.

In open-cut mining the excavation generally followed the more or less vein-like bodies of ore. Sufficient quantities of wash and lump ores were often mixed with the clayey overburden to justify passing through the washery all the material removed from the excavation on all sides of the main ore body. When a pit was first opened, and in all of the shallower mines, mule- or horse-drawn carts were used to haul the ore out of the mine hole. As the pits became deeper, inclined tracks were laid and the ore was hauled up in small ore buggies, then taken to the washery where it was prepared for market.

In those mines where shafts were sunk, the vein-like ore bodies were followed in drifts, or horizontal passageways. If various levels were to be mined, stopes were raised to the levels above for the removal of the ore. When the body of ore that was being followed became lean or disappeared, crosscuts were made to either side to try to trace the vein. While the methods employed were somewhat

94

Washed ore being loaded into mule-drawn wagons for delivery to the Saucon works of the Thomas Iron Company. Circa 1895. *C.L. Bartholomew Collection.*

Hoisting ore from shaft operations at Minesite in Lower Macungie Township, Lehigh County. Circa 1895. *Courtesy Lehigh County Historical Society.*

haphazard, pockets of good ore were usually found after several attempts.

The loose clays through which the shafts and drifts were dug were in virtually constant motion from the time mining started until the openings were filled by caving-in when mining ceased. Therefore, these openings had to be very carefully timbered both to protect the lives of miners and to keep the mine in operation. The shafts were lined with heavy, interlocking timbers generally arranged to form a rectangle conforming to the desired shaft dimensions. Heavy planks, often two or more inches thick, were driven behind the interlocking timbers and wedged against the side of the shaft to provide a completely tight lining to prevent loose materials from falling down the shaft. The vertical distance between the rectangular frameworks of heavy timbers varied due to local soil conditions but was usually not more than four to six feet. Vertical support posts were placed between each succeeding timbered framework so that when the shaft was extended to the maximum depth to be worked, the whole reinforcing framework would be supported on a footer of hard clay or rock at the base of the shaft as well as being wedged against itself and the clay sidewalls. The shaft was lined from the surface downwards so that at no time during its construction would more than four to six feet of unsupported material be exposed to endanger the lives of the miners. The shafts in larger operations were frequently divided into three compartments, two for the cages in which the ore cars or buckets were raised and lowered, and the other for piping and for the ladders by which the miners descended to the diggings. A small shelter, or hoist house, was erected over the shaft head to protect both the hoisting machinery and the shaft itself from the elements. In the very earliest mines the hoists were probably operated by horsepower, but by the time any deep shafts were sunk, portable steam engines were available for both hoisting and pumping.

In the underground mines, the drifts were first dug on the lowest level that was to be worked. These passageways were reinforced and supported in the same basic manner as the vertical shafts so that the only unsupported area was the mine face where the ore was dug. If higher levels were to be worked, a vertical or nearly vertical shaft, about five feet square, was dug upwards to the proposed level of the higher drift and the tunnel was then extended in either direction to follow the ore body. This vertical shaft connecting the upper and lower drifts was then lined with heavy cribbing, usually six-inch square timbers, and became the ore chute down which the ore was dumped to the lowest level, from which it was removed from the mine. A plank hopper was constructed at the bottom of the lowest ore chute and fitted with a gate so that small narrow-gauge

96

ore cars could be run underneath it and filled with ore. In some mines the ore was loaded directly into cars and the whole car was hoisted to the surface and dumped; in others, the ore was loaded into buckets resting on a flat car and only the buckets were hoisted to the surface.

Risers were constructed between the various levels to allow passage from one level to another for miners, tools, equipment, and supplies. These risers were approximately three to four feet square and were generally lined with four-inch-square cribbing. Most deep mines were sufficiently small so that the only ventilation required was provided by the mine shaft. However, at the larger mines in the Ironton area in Lehigh County, which were worked over a longer period of time, ventilator shafts were sunk to provide fresh air to the longer drifts. In the lowest drift, where the air was relatively fresh and where the ore loaders were constantly on the move, light was provided by small kerosene-fueled miners' lamps, the same as those used by nineteenth-century coal miners. For the ore diggers working at a mine face in a drift some distance from the main shaft, where ventilation was something less than optimum, the preferred light source was a candle set upon some portion of the reinforcing timberwork. The candles did not give off the noxious smoky fumes as did the burning "coal oil" in the miners' lamps; in the relatively draft-free atmosphere of the drift, they generally provided adequate light for the diggers' tasks.

Water was encountered in most mines, even in the open-pit type. Sometimes the flow was great enough to create a serious obstacle that had to be overcome if operations were to continue. However, most often the flow could be handled by pumping; sumps were dug in the lowest level of the mine and the water thus collected was pumped to the surface where it was used for washing the ore. In shaft-type mines, the sumps were dug below the lowest working level and a steam-driven pump was installed in a small room constructed off the main shaft, at a higher level. The coal-fired boilers remained above ground and the steam was piped down the shaft to the pumping engine.

If water was not encountered in the mine itself, separate wells had to be dug, or water pumped from a nearby stream, because water was essential for the preparation of the ore for shipment. While in a few mines masses of relatively pure ore were obtained that were practically free from adhering clay, this was the exception. In most cases the sticky clay clung so tenaciously to the ore that the material had to be passed twice through the washer before it was suitable for shipment.

The washeries employed variations of the common log washer, basically a primitive form of screw conveyer, similar in appearance to those used in grist mills for the horizontal conveyance of grains. The conveyer was constructed from a log of uniform diameter, twenty feet or more in length, into which iron plates were hammered or lag-bolted in a spiral arrangement along its entire length. The plates protruded a few inches from the outside diameter of the log and were spaced closely enough so that no sizable piece of ore might pass through. The washer shaft was set into an inclined trough constructed from heavy planks and was supported at each end by a wooden bearing surface so that the plates nearly touched the sides and bottom of the trough when the log was rotated. At the head of the washer trough, water was introduced from either a pipe or a small trough. The ore was placed in the low end of the washery trough. As the rotating log conveyed it to the upper end, it passed through the stream of water that carried away the clay and any pieces of ore and gravel small enough to pass between the iron plates. Not all of the material that reached the head of the washer was iron ore, so an operator, commonly referred to as the "gravel picker," was stationed there to pick out and discard clay clods, pieces of chert, stones, and any other unwanted materials. The wastewater was carried via troughs supported by light-duty wood trestles either to a settling pond or to a nearby worked-out pit. In areas where washer water was at a premium, a series of settling basins were constructed and the comparatively clear water from the last basin was pumped and recycled through the washery. Many of the earlier pits are no longer easily recognizable as mining sites because they were used as repositories for silt and other waste materials from adjacent washery operations. However, many homeowners in the Valley have become intimately aware of their locations when they attempt to plant a garden in the yellow clay soil of their backyards.

The pattern of ownership of the limonite deposits was diverse. All of the local iron companies owned and operated at least three or four mines. Others were owned by small local mining companies or by farmers who operated one or more mines on their own property. The large multi-furnace companies, such as the Thomas Iron Company, Crane Iron Company, Allentown Iron Company, Bethlehem Iron Company, and Glendon Iron Company, often owned and operated dozens of mines. By doing so, they had direct knowledge of operating costs. Because they were also the major customers of the independent operators, the large iron producers effectively determined the market price of ore and the wages of the miners. In times of strong demand for iron, ore prices, wages, and profits were high. When times turned "dull," prices fell, wages were cut, and profits disappeared. The less productive mines were then shut down, sometimes forever, but often to return to operation when iron prices rebounded.

Washery plant at Smith's Mine near Fogelsville, Lehigh County, looking east. This mine was opened by the Millerstown Iron Company in the 1870s and continued by its successor, the Macungie Iron Company, into the 1880s. The boilers are in the low building with stacks. The steam engine is housed in the taller structure closest to the logwasher. Circa 1887. *Courtesy Elizabeth W. Moatz.*

View of the Smith Mine's washery, looking from east to west. The water tank is just to the left of the gravel picker's shack at the head of the wash trough. The ore was delivered by a chute to the loading bins behind the men in the foreground. Circa 1887. *Courtesy Elizabeth W. Moatz.*

Getting the ore from the widely scattered mines to the furnaces along the Lehigh River was a very difficult task prior to construction of the railroads. Horse-drawn wagons were the only means. As iron companies expanded, building additional and larger furnaces, this became increasingly unsatisfactory. Massive traffic jams clogged the roads to the furnaces, as described in the 1914 History of Catasauqua: "Ore for the furnaces was hauled by heavy teams from various mines throughout the County. A line of teams nearly a mile in length was a customary sight. During rainy seasons, the 'ore roads' became well nigh impassable."

The situation was worst along the Lehigh River from Coplay downstream to Allentown, a five-mile stretch that contained a dozen blast furnaces by 1855. The only way to relieve the congestion was by building a railroad to the ore districts. The lead was taken by the Thomas Iron Company of Hokendauqua and the Crane Iron Company of Catasauqua, which together sought a charter for a railroad from Catasauqua to Fogelsville. The 1914 History of Catasauqua describes this as a less than universally popular quest:

> The application for this charter was presented to the Legislature by Mr. James W. Fuller, Sr. His efforts met with intense opposition. Indignation meetings were called and the efforts of the "Black Republicans" bitterly denounced. It was claimed that a railroad would cut up and destroy the beautiful farming districts of the Jordan Valley, and be a source of terror to beasts and danger to man. By perseverance and tact, Mr. Fuller succeeded at last in securing a charter for the construction of a plank road on the common highway of the ore-teams. A short distance of the plank road was built. Soon planks were forced out of place by the weight of the loads hauled, others broke and splintered until the road became very dangerous and, especially for pleasure carriages, nigh impassable. After prolonged efforts, the railroad charter was secured, and the construction of the "Catasauqua and Fogelsville R.R." begun in the spring of 1856. The formal opening of the road as far as Rupp's station followed during the summer of 1857. The extension of the road to the mountain at Rittenhouse Gap, the field of magnetic ore-mines, was completed later [in 1864].

Ore wharves were constructed at various locations along the railroads for loading ore onto railroad cars. The Catasauqua and Fogelsville Railroad had been built primarily for carrying ore and so had wharves along its right-of-way, as did the East Pennsylvania Railroad, a line between Reading and Allentown that was completed in 1859, and the North Pennsylvania Railroad, whose route from

Philadelphia to South Bethlehem, completed in 1857, traversed the Saucon Valley.

The ore was hauled to the wharves on wagons pulled by two-, four-, or six-horse or mule teams, weighed and then unloaded onto long heaps and mountains over the wharf. The ore wagons, which had removable slats in the bottom, were dragged up onto the heaps where the slats were pulled and the load thus deposited. Every day one or two cars were shifted onto the siding alongside the wharves, where loaders filled the cars by hand. The next day they were moved on out to the furnaces.

In Lower Macungie Township in west central Lehigh County, limonite mining was intensive from 1855 through the end of the nineteenth century. More than 80 mines were in operation during this period to serve the nearby furnaces at Alburtis, Macungie, and Emmaus. Ore was sent also to the furnaces of the large iron companies along the Lehigh River. Ore wharves were constructed along both the East Pennsylvania and the Catasauqua and Fogelsville rights-of-way. The largest ore wharves in the township were located east of the old Smith's Crossing in East Macungie. Two long ore wharves were constructed along the northern side of the East Pennsylvania Railroad right-of-way and when both wharves were in operation the huge heaps of ore stretched for half a mile along the railroad tracks. The first and westernmost of these two wharves was owned and operated by the Allentown Iron Company; the office and weighing station associated with it were located next to Smith's Crossing. This wharf, opened in 1863, was managed by Aquila Knauss, who served as agent and weighmaster until the company finally abandoned the operation late in the nineteenth century.

The easternmost, and newer, wharf at East Macungie was managed for many years by Charles Gross. It was operated for the more distant iron companies and was abandoned long before the first wharf. A half mile west of the borough of Macungie, near the Gehman Road Crossing over the East Penn Division tracks (of the Philadelphia and Reading Railroad), was another wharf known as Shiffert's. It was established long after those at East Macungie, and closed down much earlier, remaining in operation for only about ten years. Another wharf was situated at Alburtis; it was located along both the north and south sides of the East Penn Division's tracks, just to the east of the depot.

The shipment of ore by railroad did not eliminate damage to local roadways; it simply changed the areas subject to destruction. The ore still had to be carted from the mines to the ore wharves. The situation in Lower Macungie was described by Oscar Penrose Knauss, publisher of The Macungie Progress and son of Aquila Knauss, manager of the ore wharf in East Macungie:

The Bittenbender Mine at Siesholtzville, Hereford Township, Berks County, a magnetite mine operated by the Reading Coal and Iron Company. A branch line from the Catasauqua and Fogelsville Railroad just north of Rittenhouse Gap was extended to serve this mine. Circa 1887. *Courtesy Elizabeth W. Moatz.*

Ore washery at Reinhard's Mine at the village of Minesite in Lower Macungie Township. An expensive residential development, Brookhaven, now occupies this extensively mined area. Many of the homes are built adjacent to, or in some cases within, the abandoned pits. The ramp leads to the head of the log washer
Courtesy Lehigh County Historical Society.

The delivery of this ore, by strings of teams, every weekday throughout the year was an interesting sight. Roads were generally poor and this continued hard wear by heavy wagons made and kept them worse. In summer especially the procession of ore trains raised clouds of dust that hung over the wagons. In winter the snow was ground up and creaked, making an eary sound.

When it rained the situation was even worse; the roads became seas of mud. The following account by Albert Ohl, taken from his History of Upper Saucon Township, describes conditions there:

The hauling was paid by the ton, therefore overloading was often the rule. Nobody not having lived in this era can half imagine the commotion. Wagons often stuck in the mud up to the axle; drivers cracking the long snake whips, with a report of revolver shots; drivers cursing to high heaven. This was certainly a hard life, but they helped each other. But it cost a lot of horses and many broken down wagons and broken harnesses. The saddlers trade was good in those days. Each teamster liked to boast of the heavy loads he could haul, but it did not pay. Bridges were broken down, roads got into terrible condition, etc.

When very large ore mines were operated by the larger iron companies, branch railroads were built. The Catasauqua and Fogelsville Railroad had numerous branch lines in Upper Macungie and South Whitehall townships. The Thomas Iron Company constructed a branch from the North Penn Railroad for more than five miles into the western part of the Saucon Valley to transport ore to its furnaces in Hellertown. These branches certainly alleviated some of the pressure on the area's roadways, such as they were.

The iron mines at Ironton, in north central Lehigh County, were so productive that a separate railroad was built to move their ore to market. These mines, opened in the early nineteenth century by Stephen Balliet to provide ore to the Lehigh (charcoal) Furnace, were operated principally by the Thomas Iron Company from the 1850s until the end of World War I. To get this ore to their furnaces at Hokendauqua, the company contracted with Tinsley Jeter, a local real estate developer and entrepreneur, to construct the Ironton Railroad. The line was chartered on June 3, 1859, and by May 24, 1860, the first loaded ore cars were transported from Ironton to the Thomas furnaces. In 1862 the Siegersville branch was added to reach the ore deposits in that vicinity. On February 1, 1882, the Thomas Iron Company acquired complete control of the Ironton Railroad and continued to realize profits from its operation, even after the ore deposits were depleted, by transporting portland cement from the mills at Coplay, Egypt, and Ormrod. During the

1920s the line was taken over by the Reading Company, which operated portions of the route until recent times.

Magnetite ore mining was never even remotely as extensive in the Lehigh Valley as was the mining of the brown hematites. The Thomas Iron Company's mines at Rittenhouse Gap, and the Reading Coal and Iron Company's mines near Siesholtzville, were fairly large operations but were never as productive as the mines in the New Jersey section of the Reading Prong. All of the local furnaces used New Jersey magnetic ores, transported first by the Morris Canal and later by the Central Railroad of New Jersey to Phillipsburg, New Jersey. From there the ore was transported to the Lehigh Valley furnaces originally on the Lehigh Navigation and later by the Lehigh Valley, the East and North Penn branches of the Philadelphia and Reading Railroad, or by the CNJ itself.

Many of the larger Lehigh Valley iron companies owned and operated mines in Morris County, New Jersey, where the ores often contained as much as 60 percent iron. However, this ore frequently contained too much phosphorus and sulfur to be used for foundry pig or in Bessemer steel production. While their sulfur content could be reduced by roasting the ores, the phosphorus remained a serious problem until the adoption of the basic openhearth process in the 1880s. The discovery of rich, low-sulfur and low-phosphorus Lake ores, from Michigan, Wisconsin, and Minnesota, had little direct impact on the Lehigh Valley. While these rich red hematites were used extensively in the Pittsburgh District and the furnaces of Ohio, Indiana, and Illinois, the eastern furnaces generally found it cheaper to import similar ores from Spain and Cuba. The importation of foreign ores, begun in the late 1870s, continues to this day. The single operating furnace of the Bethlehem plant of the Bethlehem Steel Corporation now uses foreign ores exclusively.

The cessation of brown hematite mining preceded the demise of the local pig industry by only a few years. Even those few merchant furnaces that survived into the 1920s discontinued the use of local limonite ores after World War I. In describing the economic considerations that led to the mine closings, Lehigh University professor Benjamin L. Miller pointed to the ores' high silica content, its variability, and an iron content averaging only 40 percent. Some ores also contained significant amounts of phosphorus. To companies trying to maximize the productivity of newer, more modern blast furnaces, these objections were too great to overcome. Miller, however, believed that "there is reason to believe that at some time mining will be actively resumed," if only after high-grade reserves are depleted. This will never happen. In 1941, when Miller reached his conclusion, the farmland on which future mines might be developed was selling for no more than a few hundred dollars an acre.

Today this farmland is being rapidly converted to housing developments where a half-acre building lot can cost as much as $70,000 and the houses often exceed $250,000.   Ore prices will never rise high enough to displace suburbia.

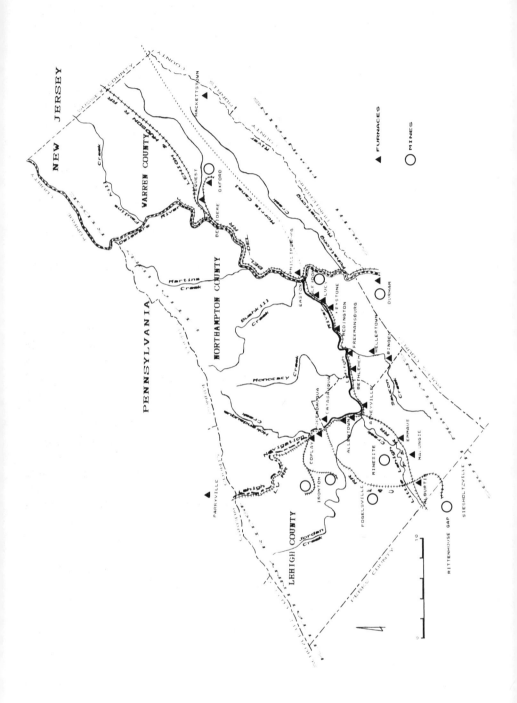

NEW JERSEY

WARREN COUNTY

PENNSYLVANIA

NORTHAMPTON COUNTY

LEHIGH COUNTY

FURNACES

MINES

CHAPTER V

GUIDE TO THE IRON FURNACES OF THE LEHIGH VALLEY

The significance of the Lehigh Valley in the development of the nation's iron industry and its industrial growth has been explored in general terms in previous chapters. A study of the individual enterprises provides a deeper understanding of the fledgling industry, its technological and economic growth, and the extent of the influence of certain families.

The brief histories that follow describe the formation and decline of each company. The furnaces of Warren County, New Jersey, are included in this survey because of their geographical proximity and commercial ties to the economy of the Lehigh Valley.

Since the Bethlehem Iron Company, the sole survivor among so many, was from its inception a specialized manufacturer and not simply a merchant pig producer, its history is examined in a separate chapter.

THE ALLENTOWN IRON COMPANY

By the mid-1840s, businessmen and merchants in the eastern seaboard cities of New York, Boston, and Philadelphia recognized the investment potential in anthracite ironmaking. One such group was the Philadelphia shipping firm of Bevan and Humphries, which sought to sponsor an iron furnace in the hope of realizing a quick return on their capital investment. Conscious of the need to choose the best location for their furnace, Messrs. Bevan and Humphries solicited the advice of veteran ironmaster Samuel Lewis, then living in Philadelphia.

Lewis was amply qualified to provide such advice, as he was familiar with both ironmaking and coal mining. He had worked under the celebrated ironmaster James Coleman at the Elizabeth Furnace in Lebanon County and for a few years prior to 1832 had served as superintendent of the Lehigh Furnace. Subsequently, he was engaged in coal mining in the Port Carbon area.

After a brief investigation during late 1845, Lewis suggested to Bevan and Humphries that Allentown, because of its proximity to both the ore fields and the Lehigh Canal, was the most suitable location for their furnace.

On April 1, 1846, Bevan and Humphries purchased 72 acres along the right bank of the Lehigh, a short distance upstream from the present Tilghman Street bridge. They ordered blowing engines and other machinery from the Philadelphia firm of Haywood & Snyder, and hired Benjamin Perry, the ironmaster who had blown in the Pioneer Furnace and many other early anthracite furnaces in the Schuylkill and Susquehanna valleys, to supervise the erection of the furnace. The first furnace was completed and successfully blown in during October, 1846; No. 2 stack was completed the following year. Both stacks were relatively small, each only 35 feet high with a 12 foot bosh. Both had open tops and their combined capacity was initially 250 tons per week.

The Allentown Iron Company in 1887. The tracks of the Lehigh Valley Railroad main line pass through the furnace property. *Courtesy Lehigh County Historical Society*.

In 1851, Bevan and Humphries sold the works to a group of eight investors from Allentown and Philadelphia who soon embarked on an expansion program. In 1854, No. 3 stack, originally 45 feet by 16 feet, was completed; No. 4, 50 feet by 16 feet, was blown in during 1855. At around the same time, stacks 1 and 2 were raised to 45 feet. A fifth furnace, the largest at 60 feet by 17 feet, was completed in 1873. By 1880, the five stacks had a combined capacity of 60,000 tons per year.

In 1885, stacks 2, 3 and 4 were abandoned and the following year a new 60 foot by 16½ foot stack, designated No. 4, was built and blown in. By 1890, coke was being mixed with anthracite and the combined capacity of the three remaining stacks reached 68,000 tons per year.

The firm never really recovered from the panic of 1893. By 1894, the obsolete No. 1 stack was abandoned and Nos. 4 and 5 were

operated only sporadically. Frequent changes in management occurred during the 1890s and are indicative of the company's economic difficulties. After 1900 the plant was operated briefly under the
management of the Crane Works of the Empire Steel and Iron Company,
but the cost of modernizing the comparatively obsolete facility was
too great. By 1904 the last furnace had been blown out and the
works dismantled for scrap.

One of the two blast furnaces of the Allentown Rolling Mill Company is visible at
the extreme right. The slag fill is encroaching on the Lehigh River. The sixth
ward of the city of Allentown lies in the background. Circa 1885.   *Courtesy
Randolph L. Kulp.*

THE ALLENTOWN ROLLING MILLS

Upon its acquisition of the Roberts Iron Company in 1871,
Allentown Rolling Mill Company achieved the distinction of becoming
the only integrated iron company to operate in Lehigh County during
the anthracite iron era. The output of its two furnaces was used
exclusively in its own mills for the manufacture of finished and
semi-finished iron products. Rolled iron "T" and street rails, fish
plates, merchant bars, angles, spikes, bolts, nuts, axles, machinery,
bridge work, and mine and flat cars were the products of the firm's
furnaces, mills, and machine shops.

In addition to the blast furnaces, the company operated 2 single
and 23 double puddling furnaces, 12 heating furnaces, and the rolling mills with 8 trains of rolls. Unlike the Bethlehem Iron Company,
however, it never installed steelmaking furnaces. Therefore, as
low-cost steel products became more readily available during the

late nineteenth and early twentieth centuries, its markets were steadily eroded and by 1912 its mills were shut down.

The Allentown Rolling Mill Company was organized in 1860 with Benjamin Haywood of Pottstown and Christian Pretz, Samuel Bridges, and John Stiles of Allentown as the principal stockholders. The company's rail mill and puddling furnaces were located along the Lehigh River, east of the Lehigh Valley Railroad tracks between Liberty and Tilghman streets. The property is now occupied by the Lehigh Structural Steel Company.

Operations were expanded in 1868 with the acquisition of the merchant bar mill of the Lehigh Rolling Mill Company. The facilities of this second company, organized by Samuel Lewis in 1861 to produce merchant bar iron and later railroad spikes and boiler rivets, lay adjacent to and slightly upstream of the Allentown Rolling Mill plant.

The Roberts Iron Company was organized in 1862 by George Algernon and Edward Roberts, Sr., of Philadelphia, A. Pardee and George Markle of Hazleton, William Lilley of Mauch Chunk, and Eli Saeger and Samuel McHose of Allentown. Two open-top stone stacks, each 68 feet by 15 feet, were built in 1864 on the site adjacent to and downstream of the Allentown Rolling Mills. These furnaces were never significantly modernized, and old-style pig iron pipe stoves were used throughout the plant's existence. Production, at first about 18,000 tons annually, was gradually increased to a maximum of 24,000 tons by the introduction of coke and richer ores.

Like most of the other local furnaces, the Allentown Rolling Mill Company was subject to cyclical trends in the economy. The furnaces were blown out for a few years in the late 1870s, and again lay idle from 1894 until around 1900. They were then operated on and off until 1907, after which they remained idle until they were dismantled in 1912-13. All operations ceased in 1912, but the company continued in existence until 1914 when the property was acquired by the Aldrich Pump Company, now owned by Ingersoll-Rand.

THE CARBON IRON COMPANY

The first furnace of the Carbon Iron Company, originally known as the Poco Anthracite Furnace, was built at Parryville, Carbon County, by Bowman Brothers and Company in 1855. The site was on the east side of the Lehigh River, on the canal at Lock No. 13 and just upstream of the mouth of Big, or Pohopoco, Creek. On August 15, 1857, the firm was incorporated as the Carbon Iron Company.

The first furnace stack was 40 feet high, with an open top and a 13 foot bosh. The original water-powered blast machinery was replaced with steam equipment in 1857; production that year was 3,217 tons of iron in a 41½-week blast. The expanding iron market of the 1860s led to the decision to construct two more furnaces; No. 2 stack, 52 by 16 feet, was built in 1864, and No. 3 stack, 65 by 16 feet, was completed in 1869. During the same period, No. 1 stack was raised to 52 feet for more efficient operation. Both of the newer stacks had closed tops to capture waste gas to heat the stoves and generate steam for the blowing engines. By 1875, the three furnaces had a combined annual capacity of 30,000 tons.

The first of the three furnaces of the Carbon Iron Company had its pipe stove on top of the furnace stack, as did many of the furnaces built before the 1860s. Circa 1865. *C.L. Bartholomew Collection.*

The borough of Parryville, Carbon County, with the Carbon Iron Company works in the background. A vertical elevator for one of the discontinued furnaces is visible beyond the roof of the pipe foundry. Circa 1895. *C.L. Bartholomew Collection.*

The single sheet-iron stack, equipped with three regenerative stoves, replaced the three masonry stacks by 1874. *Courtesy C.L. Bartholomew Collection.*

Economic conditions during the 1870s led to the firm's reorganization in 1876 as the Carbon Iron and Pipe Company, Ltd. A cast iron pipe foundry was added to the works in 1883-1884, and in the early 1890s a modernization program was undertaken. No. 1 stack was dismantled in 1893, and a year later No. 2 was scrapped. In 1893-1894, No. 3 stack was completely rebuilt; when completed, it was 66 feet high with a 15 foot bosh, and was equipped with three 70- by 18-foot Cowper-Foote regenerative stoves.

This comparatively modern rebuilt furnace plant had an annual capacity of 38,000 gross tons, more than the combined capacity of the three earlier stacks. Three types of pig iron were produced under the following brand names: foundry iron - "Carbon"; Bessemer iron - "Parry"; and low-phosphorus iron - "Viking" and "Vasa."

Originally, the ores used were limonite from Lehigh County and magnetite from New Jersey and Lake Champlain; late in the 1890s, Lake and foreign hematites were introduced. These richer ores, together with the introduction of larger quantities of coke, later increased the annual capacity to 40,000 tons.

The firm was reorganized in February, 1892, as a limited partnership with no change in its name. In September, 1917, it was again reorganized, and was renamed the Carbon Furnace Company. The furnace was relined in 1918 and remained in operation for five more years; the final cast was made in August, 1923.

A visit to the furnace site, which is presently occupied by a ready-mix concrete plant operated by the Rock Hill Materials Company, reveals almost no evidence of earlier ironmaking activities. Only a remnant of the once-extensive slag dump remains, the bulk of the slag having been quarried away for road ballast used in the construction of the Northeast Extension of the Pennsylvania Turnpike, whose bridge over the Lehigh River passes directly over the site.

THE COLERAINE IRON COMPANY

The Coleraine Iron Works was founded in 1868 by entrepreneur William T. Carter, a Cornish immigrant who had amassed a fortune as a business partner in the coal operations of Lehigh Valley Railroad magnate Asa Packer. Located in a former limestone quarry adjacent to the tracks of the Lehigh Valley Railroad on the south bank of the Lehigh River between Bethlehem and Glendon, this site was named Redington after the family name of Carter's wife. The iron company itself was named after the most prosperous of Carter's anthracite mines.

In 1869, Carter erected a sheet-iron blast furnace that was 60 feet high and had a 17-foot diameter bosh. In 1871, an additional furnace of similar dimensions was added. The two furnaces had a combined annual production capacity of 26,000 tons of iron. Two traditional pipe stoves heated the air for the hot blast.

During the early 1870s, Carter added machine shops and a foundry to his production facilities. These new facilities allowed the firm to produce parts for other Lehigh District iron manufacturers, in addition to pig iron. Redington itself soon grew into a sizable community, possessing workers' homes, a church, a school, a post office, a hotel, and a company store that did an annual business of over $35,000. during the 1870s.

To provide iron ore for his furnaces, Carter had initially purchased ten iron mines; four were located in Northampton County, six in Lehigh and Berks counties. He also brought in quantities of New Jersey iron ores via the Lehigh Valley Railroad. Typically, the Coleraine Iron Company's furnaces used a charge consisting of 5/8 Pennsylvania irons (mainly limonite and hematites) and 3/8 New Jersey magnetite. The limestone flux was quarried at Redington while the anthracite to fuel the furnaces was brought from his mines.

By 1890-1891, the Coleraine Iron Company had increased the capacity of its furnaces to produce over 40,000 tons of iron annually. The company employed over 200 men at its production facilities while an equal number were employed in auxiliary operations at Redington.

A pair of ten-inch guns at the Redington Proving Grounds of the Bethlehem Iron Company in 1892. The company used these guns to test its armor plate in the proving grounds, an abandoned limestone quarry adjacent to the former site of the Coleraine Furnace. The armor-plate target is in the right background. *John Fritz Collection, Hugh Moore Historical Park and Museums, Inc., Easton, Pa.*

Close-up view of the armor plate in previous photo. The plate was not penetrated by hits from five ten-inch shells

John Fritz Collection, Hugh Moore Historical Park and Museums, Inc., Easton, Pa.

The death of William Carter and the onset of the panic of 1893 marked the end of pig iron production at Redington. However, a portion of the facility was taken over in 1902 by the Adams Crucible Company, which employed a five-unit Swindell steel melting furnace, two cementing furnaces, and a 700-pound and a 1500-pound drop hammer to produce high quality tool steel and specialized steel castings. This company had an annual production capacity of 1,350 tons; it operated until 1908 when it was reorganized as the Redington Steel Company, which closed down in 1915.

A more important use of the Redington site was developed by the Bethlehem Iron Company. Beginning in 1887, the Bethlehem Iron Company leased an abandoned quarry at Redington for use as a proving ground for its cannon and, later, armor plate. Cannon of various sizes were tested regularly, including large caliber naval guns. The proving grounds remained in operation until 1918. During World War I, Bethlehem expanded its use of the Redington site by building an artillery-shell production facility. This plant operated between the years 1916 and 1918; it consisted of four large wooden buildings on concrete foundations, three prefabricated wooden offices, an electrical shop, a chemical laboratory, several storage buildings, and guard houses. The facility was capable of producing over 2,500 shells daily. The majority of the shells produced were of 9.2- and 8-inch sizes. Many 250-millimeter shells were also made there. Over 600 workers were employed by Bethlehem at Redington during World War I. In 1919, the entire facility was shut down. Portions of it were occupied by the Redington Standard Fittings Corporation until 1921, when the buildings were torn down and the site abandoned. The only remains at Redington are the ruins of the blowing engine house of the Coleraine Furnace, and several inactive quarries.

COOPER FURNACE-ANDOVER IRON COMPANY

The development of the Andover Iron Company at Phillipsburg, New Jersey, began in 1847 when the firm of Cooper and Hewitt purchased 40 acres of land adjacent to the Morris Canal to construct an anthracite-fueled ironmaking facility. The site was chosen because of its proximity to the junction of the Morris Canal with the Lehigh Navigation system and the Delaware Canal in nearby Easton, Pennsylvania. All three of these waterways had important functions in Cooper and Hewitt's plans for the Phillipsburg plant. The Morris Canal would bring in iron ore from the firm's mines at Andover, New Jersey; the Lehigh Navigation would bring in anthracite; and the Delaware Canal would provide a means of transporting the pig iron that would be produced at Phillipsburg to Cooper and Hewitt's rail mills at Trenton, New Jersey.

The Andover Furnace about 1870. The Morris Canal and the Belvidere and Delaware Railroad are in the foreground. *James Lee Collection, Phillipsburg, N.J.*

The Andover Furnace, as seen from the Belvidere and Delaware Railroad. *James Lee Collection, Phillipsburg, N.J.*

Between 1849 and 1850 two stone stacks were built at Phillips-burg. These furnaces were 55 feet in height and had boshes 20 feet in diameter. In 1850, 105 men were employed and the furnaces produced 6,252 tons of pig iron. A third furnace of similar dimensions was added in 1852-1853 raising the annual production capacity to 25,000 tons. In 1855, No. 1 produced 7,980 tons of iron and No. 3 produced 7,423 tons. In 1856, No. 2's production was 7,041 tons. Additional sources of ore were developed at the firm's Ringwood property near the New Jersey-New York border to satisfy the increased production capacity. The Morris Canal remained the main transportation route for iron ore coming into Phillipsburg. During the late 1850s, the connecting Jersey Central, Lehigh Valley, and Belvidere and Delaware railroads largely supplanted the canals as the primary transportation facilities for bringing in raw materials and shipping out finished products.

It is believed that as early as 1856 the firm conducted a test of the Bessemer steelmaking process at Phillipsburg, but this experiment proved to be a failure. By 1859, the Phillipsburg plant had further increased its capacity and, according to U.S. census figures, its three furnaces were listed as having dimension of 55 by 20 feet, 42 by 18 feet and 55 by 22 feet respectively. The Phillipsburg furnaces were among the most productive in America that year.

The furnace at Phillipsburg supplied the iron that was shipped to the Trenton Iron Company to be converted into wrought iron and rolled into some of the earliest structural beams in America. These beams were used in 1854-1857 for the construction of the Cooper Union of New York City.

During the Civil War, iron from the Phillipsburg furnaces was sent to Trenton where it provided the raw material for gun metal that was used to produce ordnance for the Union Army.

In 1867, the furnaces at Phillipsburg and the Andover and other New Jersey iron ore mines were sold to a group of Pennsylvania capitalists that included the Hazleton coal magnate, Ario Pardee. Reorganized as the Andover Iron Company, the furnaces were upgraded by the addition of two new and more powerful blowing engines. By 1881, the Andover Iron Company had three large iron-shell furnaces in operation at Phillipsburg with an annual production capacity of 50,000 tons. Early in the twentieth century, the Andover Iron Company was purchased by the Wharton Steel Company, which operated only one furnace at the Phillipsburg site. Joseph Wharton, a Philadelphia entrepreneur, had been a major stockholder in the Bethlehem Iron Company prior to 1901. He owned several furnaces and extensive iron ore lands in many parts of New Jersey.

In 1910, the plant was entirely shut down and in 1912 it was purchased by the Pennsylvania Railroad to allow for the expansion of its lower Belvidere and Delaware Division yard at Phillipsburg. In 1917, almost all of the buildings at the site were demolished, although the office building survived as a ruin into the 1980s. The site is now occupied by the Andover-Morris elementary school.

THE CRANE IRON COMPANY

The Crane Iron Company was the first and one of the last of the merchant pig producers to operate in the Lehigh Valley. To a large extent its long life was due to the able management of David Thomas and his successors. In 1855, upon the completion of the Thomas Works in Hokendauqua, 15 years after the first successful commercial use of anthracite to make iron at the Crane Works in Catasauqua, David Thomas relinquished the superintendency of the Crane Works to his son John. The younger Thomas served as superintendent until 1867, when he left the Crane Iron Company to become general superintendent of the Thomas Iron Company. He was succeeded by his brother-in-law, Joshua Hunt, who remained superintendent until January 1, 1882.

During Hunt's tenure, numerous improvements were made to the plant. In 1868, No. 6 stack, 60 feet high with a bosh diameter of 17½ feet, was erected; it was the last Crane furnace built with iron pipe stoves. In 1877, No. 5 stack was rebuilt and equipped with three Whitwell regenerative fire-brick stoves. In 1879, No. 3 stack collapsed while it was out of blast, leading to a decision to remove the three oldest stacks and erect new ones on the sites of No. 1 and No. 3, and to place Whitwell fire-brick stoves on the ground formerly occupied by stack No. 2. The new No. 1 was 75 feet by 18 feet, and No. 3 was 65 by 17 feet; both were constructed in 1880 and blown in in 1881. With these improvements, the capacity of the five stacks became 100,000 net tons per year.

In 1889, No. 3 was raised to 75 feet: it continued in use until late 1913, when it was dismantled. No. 4 was blown out in July, 1890, and a few years later was dismantled. In 1901, No. 1 stack was rebuilt to 77½ by 17 feet 4 inches, and was equipped with three modern Cowper stoves. In 1907-1908, No. 5 was torn down and a new furnace, designated No. 2, was erected on its site. It was 80 by 17½ feet, and also was equipped with three Cowper stoves.

Thomas Edison selected the Crane Iron Company to test the suitability of his iron ore concentrate which he produced from low-grade iron ore at a plant near Franklin, New Jersey. After much experimentation, Edison had devised a method of concentrating ore by combining the use of massive rock crushers with magnetic separation. The company used 25,000 tons of the concentrate with great success during the 1890s. However, the high cost of Edison's

The Crane Iron Company, circa 1870. The blowing engines were in the large building.
Pennsylvania Canal Society Collection, Canal Museum, Easton, Pa.

The boat basin at the Crane works, circa 1896. Canal boats continued to deliver raw materials for many years after the first railroads were built. The building with the rounded roof is the engine house. *Hugh Moore Historical Park and Museums, Inc. Easton, Pa.*

concentrate relative to the newly developed Mesabi ores caused his plant to be shut down.

By 1914, when there were only two furnaces remaining, the combined capacity was 140,000 tons. In 1920, No. 2 was completely rebuilt. Its larger size, 90 by 20½ feet, and the more powerful blowing engines that were installed, raised the plant's capacity to 185,000 tons. One year later the Cowper stoves were replaced with four Roberts stoves, three of them with dimensions of 90 by 18 feet, the fourth 100 by 20 feet. At that time, a Pittsburgh Coal Washer Company double strand pig casting machine was installed.

The Crane Iron Company was the first in the Lehigh Valley to adopt regenerative stoves. Whitwell stoves were installed for No. 5 stack in 1887 and for the rebuilt Nos. 1 and 2 furnaces in 1880. Note the contrasting furnace designs. Cars from the Philadelphia and Reading Railroad and the Lehigh and Susquehanna Division of the Central Railroad of New Jersey are on the trestles to be unloaded. Circa 1897.

Courtesy Hugh Moore Historical Park and Museums, Inc., Easton, Pa.

No. 1 stack was dismantled in December, 1922, and the capacity of the sole remaining stack was 135,000 tons per year. While this furnace was as modern as any operating at the Bethlehem Steel Company, the postwar depression in the iron market eventually took its toll and it was last operated in 1930. The plant then lay idle until 1932, when the whole complex was dismantled for scrap.

Throughout its last years, the Crane Works was controlled by the Empire Steel and Iron Company. This organization, chartered in New Jersey on March 13, 1899, with headquarters in Catasauqua after June 1, 1900, was the creation of Leonard Peckitt, a Yorkshireman who emigrated to the United States in 1882 and entered the employment of the Reading Iron Company, where he served as chemist until 1888. In that year he came to Catasauqua to become chemist for the Crane Iron Company. His subsequent career was nothing short of phenomenal. From 1890 on he moved upward until by 1898 he became president and general manager.

Within a year after its organization, the Empire Steel and Iron Company had acquired control of the Gem Furnace in Shenandoah, Virginia, the two stacks of the Henry Clay Furnaces in Reading, the Macungie Furnace, the Topton Furnace, the Nittany Furnace in Bellefonte, the Oxford Furnace in Oxford, New Jersey, the Victoria Furnace in Goshen, Virginia, and the Cherokee Furnace in Greensboro, North Carolina. These furnaces, along with the Crane Works, had a combined annual capacity of 378,000 gross tons.

The Empire Steel and Iron Company also owned 2,500 acres of iron-ore land at Oxford, New Jersey and had mineral rights on another 8,000 acres. In 1899 it purchased the Mount Hope Mining Company, consisting of a 1,700-acre tract with magnetite ore mines and a concentrating plant with an annual capacity of 225,000 tons per year at Mount Hope, New Jersey. In conjunction with these mines, it operated the 4½-mile Mount Hope Mineral Railroad, which had connections with the Central Railroad of New Jersey and the Delaware, Lackawanna and Western Railroad at Wharton, New Jersey. To assure a steady supply of coke for its furnaces, it acquired control of the Victoria Coal & Coke Company, which owned 1,500 acres of coal lands and 135 beehive coke ovens at Caperton, West Virginia. The southern furnaces were retained for only a few years and the Macungie and Henry Clay furnaces were shut down in 1913.

Between 1919 and 1924, Peckitt reorganized and consolidated his small empire. On November 6, 1919, the Replogle Steel Company acquired the Wharton Steel Company, which merged with Replogle on March 1, 1922. In April, 1922, Replogle acquired a large interest in the capital stock of the Empire Steel and Iron Company. The entire capital stock of the Crane Iron Works was then purchased by the Warren Pipe and Foundry Company, which in turn passed under the control of Replogle Steel Company in August, 1924. However, within another five years the empire was largely a paper one. By 1930 all ironmaking operations had ceased, and the plants were dismantled shortly thereafter. The only significant resource of the successor organization, the Warren Pipe and Foundry Corporation, was the historic magnetite property at Mount Hope, New Jersey.

DURHAM FURNACE

Ironmaking in Upper Bucks County spanned a period of nearly two centuries. Several bloomeries are believed to have been in operation before 1725, producing iron from the abundant local red hematite ores. The first Durham Furnace was built in 1727 on the Durham Creek about 1½ miles to the west of its junction with the Delaware River. It was in full operation by 1728. The pig made there as well as the products of two nearby forges, was shipped to the port of Philadelphia by vessels which became known as Durham boats. Approximately eight feet in width and generally sixty feet in length, Durham boats could carry up to five tons of cargo and these vessels soon became the standard freight-carrying craft on the Delaware River. The Durham boat design was copied and modified for use on the Schuylkill River in Pennsylvania and later, the Mohawk River in New York. After the American Revolution, Durham boats were built and operated on Canada's Ottawa and St. Lawrence rivers.

The original Durham Furnace used charcoal for fuel and employed a water-powered cold-air-blast blowing system. Its early owners included some of the most prominent leaders of colonial Pennsylvania, such as Anthony Morris, William Allen, Joseph Turner, James Logan, Israel Pemberton, and Joseph Galloway. The Durham Furnace produced shot and shells for British and Colonial forces fighting in the French and Indian War and during the American Revolution it produced both cannon and ammunition for the Continental Army. During both of these conflicts, Durham Furnace was managed by George Taylor, who became a signer of the Declaration of Independence and a prominent patriot leader. It should also be noted that General Daniel Morgan, the noted leader of riflemen at such Revolutionary War battles as Quebec, Saratoga and Cowpens, was born at Durham Furnace in 1736.

The original Durham Furnace remained in blast until 1789. By 1791, the site had been largely abandoned and many of its casting patterns and other equipment had been sold to the owners of the Hibernia Furnace in New Jersey. Early in the nineteenth century a grist mill was erected on the site of the first Durham Furnace.

122

Durham Iron Works in 1870. The masonry 1848 and 1851 stacks were demolished in 1873-1874 and replaced by a modern sheet-iron blast furnace. *Pennsylvania Canal Society Collection, Canal Museum, Easton, Pa.*

The sheet iron furnace completed in 1874 and blown in during February, 1876, represented the third generation of ironmaking at Durham. The plant was considered state of the art when first completed but was soon eclipsed by the ever larger and more technologically advanced furnaces built in the Pittsburgh area just a few years later. Small buggies loaded with pigs can be seen alongside the cast house. Circa 1885. *Courtesy Lehigh County Historical Society.*

In 1848-1849, two anthracite-fueled stone blast furnaces were erected near the mouth of the Durham Creek by the firm of Joseph Whitaker and Company. These furnaces were termed No. 1 and No. 2.

The dimensions of Furnace No. 1 were 40 by 13 feet, while Furnace No. 2 had dimensions of 40 by 14 feet. Both of these furnaces were equipped with horizontal steam-driven blowing engines and hot blast stoves. Each of these furnaces was capable of producing 5,000 tons of iron annually. The anthracite fuel for these blast furnaces was brought in by the Delaware Canal while vessels on this same waterway shipped out the company's products.

The anthracite furnaces were originally managed by James A. Pennypacker until his death in 1851. Joseph R. Whitaker, the son of the firm's principal owners, became the next manager of Durham until he was replaced by his brother, George W. Whitaker, who continued in charge until the complex was sold to the firm of Cooper and Hewitt in 1864.

The managing partners of Cooper and Hewitt were Edward Cooper and Abram S. Hewitt, the son and son-in-law, respectively, of Peter Cooper, the noted inventor, manufacturer, and philanthropist. Edward Cooper was a brilliant engineer and pioneering ironmaster, while Abram S. Hewitt was a noted businessman who played a large role in the introduction of both Bessemer and open hearth steelmaking technology into America. However, Cooper and Hewitt made little use of the Durham facilities at that time and in 1865 sold the ironmaking complex to the firm of Lewis Lillie and Son of Troy, New York, which manufactured safes and bank vaults. Lillie transferred its entire operation to Durham and upgraded the plant by building a 61 by 92 foot foundry, a finishing plant, and new workers' housing. Despite this investment, the firm's operations were not a success and in 1867 it was taken over by its creditors who operated it until 1870 when it was sold at a sheriff sale to Cooper and Hewitt.

Cooper and Hewitt were already the owners of substantial ironmaking operations which included, at one time or another, the Trenton Iron Company at Trenton, New Jersey, and the Cooper Furnace at Phillipsburg, New Jersey. They had already made technological history in 1854 by rolling, at Trenton, the first wrought-iron structural beams to be successfully produced in America. Cooper and Hewitt proceeded to make a considerable investment at Durham. Between 1873 and 1874, they demolished the existing stone anthracite fueled blast furnaces and replaced them with a new sheet-iron stack. The stack rested on a mantle, supported by eight iron columns. This new anthracite furnace was 75 feet high and had a 20-foot bosh; it had a production capacity of over 20,000 tons of iron per year, making it one of the largest and most productive in the

Locomotive pulling slag car from Durham Furnace to the slag dump.   Circa 1885.
Courtesy Lehigh County Historical Society.

The Durham anthracite furnaces were all built on the bank of Durham (now Cook's) Creek, on the site now occupied by a defunct paper mill.   The bridge across the creek is to the right of the cast house.   The elevator and cast house of one of the earlier anthracite furnaces are visible to the left of the new engine house.   Circa 1885.   *Courtesy Lehigh County Historical Society.*

Lehigh Region. By the late 1870s, coke was also being used to supplement anthracite.

The Durham Furnace had two vertical blowing engines and eight Cooper Durham stoves. This sophisticated stove, developed by Edward Cooper at Durham, raised the temperature of the blast to a higher degree than any other form of pipe stove in general use. Since Durham stoves were cheaper to build than fire brick stoves, they were adopted by other iron companies in the Lehigh Region. As late as 1910, Durham stoves remained in operation at Lehigh Valley plants, long after modern regenerative-type stoves had been generally adopted.

Cooper introduced other innovations at Durham, including a double charging bell that prevented the escape of dangerous furnace gases, and the Luermann "closed" furnace front. Cooper also pioneered the use of bronze for tuyeres and casting notches.

The firm of Cooper and Hewitt introduced innovative metallurgical practices by employing a full-time chemist at Durham after 1870. Among these early chemists was Benjamin Franklin Fackenthal, Jr., who became superintendent at Durham in 1876. In 1893, Fackenthal would leave to become president of the Thomas Iron Company. This investment in the employment of a chemist soon paid a profitable dividend when analysis showed that Durham ore was low in phosphorus and suitable for sale to Bessemer steel plants. By 1874, this product was being produced and shipped to such pioneering steel works as the Cambria at Johnstown, the Pennsylvania Steel Company near Harrisburg, and the firm of Winslow, Griswold and Company at Troy, New York.

The shipping facilities at Durham were greatly improved during the 1870s, when a connection was made across the Delaware River to the Belvidere and Delaware Division of the Pennsylvania Railroad in New Jersey. A steam-operated inclined plane was built from the company's dock on the Delaware Canal to a stock area adjacent to the vertical charging elevators. The plane and dock were linked to the railroad by means of a siding to a cable ferry across the river. This system functioned effectively until 1896, when it was replaced by a connection with the recently built Quakertown and Easton Railroad which reached Durham from the west.

The facilities remained in successful operation until 1892, when the furnace was shut down. It was blown in again in 1899 by General Superintendent John Fackenthal. In 1900, the facilities at Durham were purchased by a new group of investors and reorganized as the Durham Iron company with Julius Christman of Philadelphia as president and John D. Thomas as superintendent. However, by 1908 the furnace was once again shut down and by 1912, it had been dismantled. The site is now occupied by a paper board plant.

The Emaus Furnace in the mid-1890s, shortly after it was leased by Robert H. Coleman of Lebanon County, who renamed it the Crumwold Furnace. Coleman replaced the original pipe stoves with three regenerative stoves before his financial failure, brought on by losses in Florida land speculation, forced him to give up the lease. The boiler house is to the right of the stoves, the engine house directly behind them. *C.L. Bartholomew Collection.*

Emaus-Crumwold Furnace from the stockhouse side. The engine house is directly behind the stockhouse. The cylindrical structure on the left side of the engine house is the cold blast receiver. Circa 1895. *C.L. Bartholomew Collection.*

The cast house of the Emaus Furnace is on the left side of the furnace stack. The structure to the left of the cast house is the pipe foundry of the Donaldson Iron Company. Circa 1895. *C.L. Bartholomew Collection.*

After the hoist house burned in 1901, the Emaus Furnace was rebuilt as a steel stack with a skip-charging system. The engine house was increased in height for a larger engine, and modifications were made to the cold blast receiver. Circa 1909. *C.L. Bartholomew Collection.*

Emaus Furnace cast house after the furnace was rebuilt. The bustle pipe and goosenecks that conveyed the hot blast to the tuyeres is clearly visible. The iron runner prepared for casting is in the foreground. To the left of the iron runner is the mud gun that was swung into place to close the tap hole after casting. *c /* *Bartholomew Collection.*

THE EMAUS-CRUMWOLD FURNACE

The Emaus Iron Company was chartered on March 11, 1870, and the stack, 68 feet high with a 16-foot bosh, was blown in on October 10, 1872. Operations were not wholly successful and the property was soon sold to the Philadelphia and Reading Coal and Iron Company. The new owners first leased the plant to the Hematite Iron Company headed by Charles H. Nimson, who at the same time was manager of the Allentown Rolling Mills. Nimson's brother-in-law, W.F. Hallman, served as superintendent. The poor iron market of the 1870s precluded profitable operations and Nimson soon gave up the lease.

The plant then lay idle for a few years until September 12, 1881, when it was blown in again by a new group of lessees operating as Ormrod, Fisher & Company. This firm consisted of George

129

Ormrod and his cousin, John Donaldson, both of whom had earlier operated collieries in the Tamaqua–Hazleton area, and two of their business associates, W.S. Thomas of Philadelphia and H.H. Fisher of Allentown. The furnace was remodeled by these lessees in 1880-81, but its operation was again unsuccessful and it was blown out again late in 1883.

In the meantime, the lessees undertook the construction of a large cast iron water-pipe and gas-pipe foundry adjacent to the furnace plant. Pipe production commenced on October 13, 1883, and continued with few interruptions until 1943. On August 9, 1886, the partnership was reorganized and incorporated as the Donaldson Iron Company with John Donaldson as president and George Ormrod as manager and treasurer. During the 1890s, Ormrod's increased interest in the cement industry forced him to leave the day-to-day management of the foundry to his subordinates. For more than half a century this foundry was the dominant industry in Emmaus, often employing as many as 500 workers.

While the foundry was an immediate success, the furnace lay idle until 1890, when it was leased by Robert H. Coleman of Lebanon who subsequently renamed the plant the Crumwold Furnace. The new lessee remodeled the furnace and equipped it with three 60 foot by 18 foot Gordon-Whitwell-Cowper regenerative stoves. These improvements increased the plant's capacity from 15,000 to 29,000 tons a year. In 1895 the Reading Iron Company acquired operating rights under a special agreement between the trustee, Robert H. Coleman, and the owner, the Philadelphia and Reading Coal and Iron Company. Albert Broden, superintendent for Coleman, continued to serve the new operators. Through better management and the introduction of greater quantities of coke, the annual capacity was soon increased to 45,000 tons.

In 1901, the hoist tower and the engine house were destroyed by fire; they were rebuilt the following year. A massive modernization program in 1909 resulted in a new 75 by 17-foot stack, three modern Roberts 80 by 20-foot stoves and two new blowing engines, all of which increased the capacity to 70,000 tons. The stack was relined in 1919 but the postwar recession led to its abandonment in 1924.

THE GLENDON IRON COMPANY

The Glendon Iron Company was the second anthracite-iron production facility to be established in the Lehigh Valley. The primary force behind the organization of this firm was Charles Jackson, Jr., an entrepreneur from Boston, Massachusetts. In 1842 Jackson secured the services of William Firmstone, the noted ironmaster, to assess the potential for making iron in the Lehigh Valley. After visiting the Valley, Firmstone reported to Jackson that the area was

130

probably the best suited for iron production in Pennsylvania and that the Lehigh Coal and Navigation Company was eager to support industrial development along the banks of its canal. Jackson authorized Firmstone to purchase land from the Lehigh Coal and Navigation Company and to secure the waterpower rights to a portion of the Company's Lehigh Navigation.

Firmstone selected a site that was located approximately two miles to the west of Easton between Section 8 of the Lehigh Navigation and the south bank of the Lehigh River. By the fall of 1842, construction had begun on the first experimental furnace of the Glendon Iron Company. By 1844, the first production furnace was completed and blown in. No. 1 Furnace was 50 feet high, and 14 by 18 feet across the bosh. Its blowing engines were powered by two 15 foot diameter waterwheels which drew their water from the adjacent Lehigh Navigation. These drove two horizontal blast cylinders. No. 2 Furnace was constructed in 1845; it was 45 feet high, and 10 by 14 feet across the bosh. In 1846, the Glendon Iron Company produced over 7,000 tons of iron. No. 3 Furnace was constructed in 1850, also 45 feet high with dimensions of 16 by 14 feet across the bosh. After 1850 a common blast, produced by a combination of water and steam power, was provided for furnaces Nos. 2 and 3.

In 1854, Jackson purchased the South Easton Furnace, which was located to the east of the main plant adjacent to the Rodenbaugh and Stewart Wire Company. This furnace had been built in 1844 by Frederick Goddell; it occupied the site of an earlier abortive cold blast charcoal furnace that had been constructed by the firm of Barnet, Swift and Company.

The Glendon Iron Company, under William Firmstone's direction, soon established a fine reputation for quality. Like many other Lehigh Valley iron companies, the Glendon Iron Company imported large quantities of New Jersey magnetite ore via the connecting Morris Canal and Lehigh Navigation. In 1852 it purchased the Teabo mine near Hibernia, N.J., which it operated until 1892. The usual furnace charge at Glendon consisted of ¼ New Jersey magnetite and ¾ local brown hematite from Williams Township.

Most of Glendon's iron was shipped via the canal network to New York, where it was loaded onto coastal schooners for shipment to Boston. There, it was rolled into bars and rolls at the Glendon Rolling Mill which was also owned by Charles Jackson, Jr. These products were then exported, or sold in New England. Unfortunately, the Glendon Rolling Mill was closed in 1857 after its superintendent had embezzled over $200,000. After 1857, the Glendon Iron Company concentrated on what became known as the Grey Forge market, where its products enjoyed a fine reputation.

The oldest known view of the Glendon Iron Company, possibly from 1849-1850, showing construction work on furnaces No. 1 and 2. The picture was taken from the inclined plane, which was used to carry slag and cinders form the furnaces to a dump in the surrounding hills. The waterwheels that powered the blowing engines were housed in the protective building in the foreground. *Collection of Canal Museum-Hugh Moore Park, Easton, Pa.*

Glendon Rolling Mill and Forge Works at East Boston, Massachusetts, from an 1855 lithograph by Henry Brevoort. Pig iron from the Glendon Furnace was shipped to this facility to be converted to wrought iron and then processed into rails and shapes. *Courtesy, Print Department, Boston Public Library.*

Glendon Iron Company in 1863. The hemispherical object between stacks is the cold blast receiver, which also acted as the roof of the engine house. Prominent in the foreground is the incline that was used to bring in ore from mines in Williams Township and to carry slag back to the mine pits. *From Peter Richards, "Two Centuries of Iron Smelting in Pennsylvania," Pennsylvania Blast Furnace Papers, 1921.*

The Glendon Iron Company in 1873 or 1874, showing the rebuilding of a furnace. The inclined plane is at the far right. *Canal Museum-Hugh Moore Park Collection, Easton, Pa.*

The Glendon Iron Company from the south bank of Section 8 of the Lehigh Navigation System. The engine house is at the extreme left; the furnace and cast house are in the center. *Canal Museum-Hugh Moore Park Collection, Easton, Pa.*

Glendon Iron Company in 1880-1881, showing several improvements to the plant, most notably the greatly enlarged engine house. Furnace No. 5 is at the extreme left. In the right foreground is the elevated narrow-gauge railroad that was constructed to carry coal and iron ore more efficiently around the plant. *Canal Museum-Hugh Moore Park Collection, Easton, Pa.*

Glendon Iron Company, looking northeast from Easton towards West Easton, showing canal boats and Lehigh Valley Railroad cars, which were used to bring in raw materials and transport pig iron to markets. *Canal Museum-Hugh Moore Park Collection, Easton, Pa.*

Rebuilt Furnace No. 1, as it appeared in 1881. Note the enlarged casting house and the inclined plane that carried raw materials to the top of the furnace. *From Peter Richards, "Two Centuries of Iron Smelting in Pennsylvania," Pennsylvania Blast Furnace Papers, 1921.*

Furnace No. 3 and its adjoining cast house. Pig iron is stacked and ready for shipment by canal boat. In 1986 several pigs of Glendon iron were recovered from the Lehigh Navigation near this spot. *Canal Museum-Hugh Moore Park Collection, Easton, Pa.*

1887 panorama of the Glendon Iron Company, seen from the north shore of the Lehigh River. The portal in the retaining wall on the extreme right was the tail race of the wheel house. *Northampton County Historical and Genealogical Society Collection, Easton, Pa.*

An oversized Lehigh Coal and Navigation Company boat at the Glendon Iron Company in 1890. These boats could operate only on the Lehigh Navigation since their width and height prevented them from entering the connecting Morris and Delaware canals. They were used solely for bringing anthracite to the furnaces in the Lehigh Valley. *James Lee Collection, Phillipsburg, N.J.*

Narrow-gauge locomotive run by William M. Morrison, with the machinist gang under B.G. Maddox. From *Sixty Seventh Anniversary of the Founding of Glendon*, Easton, Pa., 1909.

A group of employees of the Glendon Iron Company in 1886. From *Sixty Seventh Anniversary of the Founding of Glendon*, Easton, Pa., 1909.

In 1857, the Company was reorganized under Pennsylvania law and additional investors were included. Among the most prominent of these was Ario Pardee, the anthracite mining magnate from Hazleton, Pennsylvania. In 1864, the Glendon Iron Company was again reorganized with additional capital.

In 1868, the Glendon Company constructed No. 5 Furnace as a part of William Firmstone's efforts to remain competitive with other Lehigh District producers such as the Crane Iron Company and the Thomas Iron Company. No. 5 Furnace had a sheet-iron stack, 75 feet high and 18 feet in diameter at the bosh; it became the most productive of the company's furnaces. During the 1870s, the Glendon Iron Company continued to prosper under the innovative and competent leadership of William Firmstone. In 1874, Firmstone rebuilt the old No. 1 Furnace to more modern specifications. The rebuilt No. 1 was 63 feet high and 18 feet in diameter at the bosh.

After Firmstone's death in 1877, the Glendon Iron Company was managed by his son, Frank. Although Frank Firmstone was a skilled engineer, he lacked his father's organizational skills. He did attempt several interesting experiments, including a series of "great blasts" which resulted in one entire year's supply of limestone (60,000 tons) for flux being quarried by a single massive explosion. Limestone was quarried this way for five years.

In 1881, Frank Firmstone rebuilt Furnace No. 2 and Furnace No. 3 to modern specifications. As rebuilt, these iron shell furnaces were both 80 feet high and 18 feet in diameter at the bosh. The Glendon Iron Company continued to be both productive and profitable until 1884, when a steady decline began which resulted in the temporary closure of the works following Frank Firmstone's resignation in 1887.

John Thomas, a former foundryman at the works, succeeded Firmstone as superintendent and modernized furnaces Nos. 1, 2 and 3 over the next two years. In 1889, John S. Fackenthal became superintendent and iron production was restarted. In 1893, new I.P. Morris Company steam-blowing engines were installed at Glendon, but the company could not return to profitability and in 1894, the works were permanently shut down. In 1896 the company was placed in the hands of its creditors, who offered the works for sale. There were no buyers. The new blowing engines were sold to the Empire Steel and iron company, and furnaces Nos. 1 and 5 were torn down. During the next twenty years, the entire complex was demolished and the land reverted to the Lehigh Coal and Navigation Company.

Today the site of the Glendon Iron Company is a part of the City of Easton's Hugh Moore Park where a few stone ruins and the base of one furnace are all that remain of the company's production facilities. However, the adjacent boroughs of Glendon, organized in

1867, and West Easton contain many fine examples of workers' housing built in the 1840s by the Glendon Iron Company, and the Firmstone family's mansion is today a part of the Easton Children's Home.

HACKETTSTOWN IRON AND MANUFACTURING COMPANY – WARREN FURNACE

The Hackettstown Iron and Manufacturing Company was founded in 1874 by local Warren County businessmen. By 1875 a single anthracite fueled sheet iron stack with 250 horsepower steam-driven blowing machinery and a closed top had been built at a site near the Delaware, Lackawanna and Western Railroad, one half mile southwest of the Hackettstown Station. The stack was 55 feet high and 15 feet in diameter at the bosh; during its first year of operations it

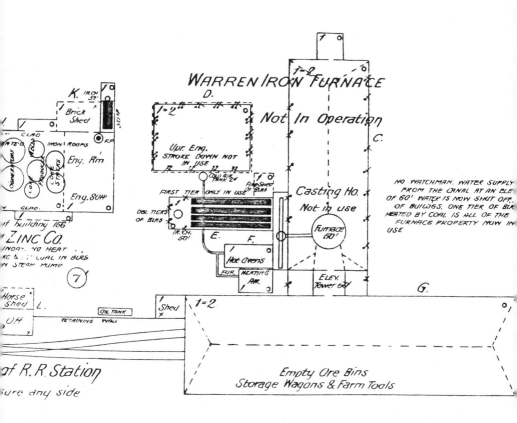

Plan of the Warren Furnace in 1892. *From the 1892 Sanborn Insurance Company map of Hackettstown, N.J.*

140

produced 10,000 tons of mill pig iron from local magnetic and Beattystown hematite ores. By 1879 production capacity had been raised to 12,000 tons per year but the company was not profitable and creditors, the Wood Brothers Company of Philadelphia, assumed control. The Wood Brothers sold it to Philadelphia entrepreneur, Joseph Wharton, who was a major stockholder in the Bethlehem Iron Company and owned extensive iron properties in New Jersey.

Wharton appointed his nephew, William Rodman Wharton, to manage the furnace. He resigned within two years and was replaced by a local ironmaster, Tooke Straker, of nearby Oxford, New Jersey. Under Straker's management the furnace continued to make mill pig iron. By 1890, annual production at the Warren Furnace was 15,000 tons of pig iron, but it was blown out for a year in 1892. It was placed back into production in 1893-1894, but it only produced 13,500 tons of iron during that period.

In 1899, the company was purchased by the newly organized Carteret Steel Company. The Hackettstown facilities were modernized and the furnace rebuilt with two new Kent stoves to supplement the original Durham stoves in heating the blast. When rebuilt, the furnace had an annual production capacity of 35,000 tons, but by 1902, it had been blown out and was placed on the market. It was never placed back into production.

THE KEYSTONE FURNACE

The Keystone Furnace was located near Chain Dam, opposite Guard Lock No. 8 on the Lehigh Navigation, at the far eastern end of the borough of Glendon. The site is presently occupied by the Ashland Chemical Company, and the foundations of the ore trestles and other facilities are still visible. The furnace was chartered as D. Runkle Company and was put into blast on April 17, 1876. Daniel Runkle, who had been a director of the Thomas Iron Company since October 16, 1873, sold the plant to the Thomas Iron Company on April 1, 1882. The Thomas Iron Company retained ownership until June 28, 1917, when it was sold to a Philadelphia firm named the Northern Ore Company. The new owners rebuilt the furnace in 1918 and operated it until April 1, 1923, when it was sold and scrapped.

This plant, one of the last merchant pig furnaces built in the Lehigh Valley, was for many years one of the most modern. The sheet-iron stack was 65 feet high with a 16-foot bosh; it was equipped with three Siemens-Cowper-Cochrane fire-brick stoves. The original capacity of the furnace is unknown, but in 1904 it was rated at 20,000 tons, in 1908 at 26,000 tons, and in 1916 and 1920 at 36,000 tons. Since there is no evidence that significant improvements were made to the plant, these figures, which appear in the directories of the American Iron & Steel Institute, are probably

The Keystone Furnace at Guard Lock No. 8 of the Lehigh Navigation System. Circa 1900. *Pennsylvania Canal Society Collection, Canal Museum, Easton, Pa.*

Stock house and charging elevator at the Keystone Furnace. The three Seimens-Cowper-Cochrane regenerative stoves are to the left of the furnace stack. Circa 1900. *Ronald Wynkoop Collection, Phillipsburg, N.J.*

The only structure standing today at the Keystone Furnace site is the superintendent's house. The Lehigh Valley Railroad's main line carried raw materials to and
pig iron from the furnace. The siding today serves the Ashland Chemical Company,
which now occupies the site. Circa 1900. *Taken from 1904 Thomas Iron Company
Annual Report.*

View of Keystone Furnace from Island Park in about 1885. *Pennsylvania Canal Society
Collection, Canal Museum, Easton, Pa.*

inflated. Certainly, the introduction of higher grade ores and high calcium stone, along with a complete conversion to coke, would have increased production significantly, but these factors were unlikely to have nearly doubled it.

Throughout most of its 47 years of operation, the Keystone Furnace remained in blast. It was blown out for a while after 1911 but was reactivated for the iron boom created by World War I.

The topography surrounding the two furnaces of the Lehigh Iron Company was so hilly that a bridge was built to transport the slag across the Lehigh River to be dumped between the river and the canal. 1891. *Courtesy Lehigh County Historical Society.*

THE LEHIGH IRON COMPANY

The Lehigh Iron Company, located at the great bend of the Lehigh River downstream from Kline's Island, was organized in 1867 by William H. Ainey, the prominent Allentown attorney, publisher and banker, who remained the firm's president until operations ceased.

No. 1 stack, 55 feet high with a 16 foot bosh, was blown in on July 22, 1869; the second stack, 60 by 17 feet, was blown in on October 21, 1872. Both open-top stacks were of masonry construction and the blast was heated by traditional iron pipe stoves. Their original combined capacity was 21,000 net tons per year. In 1886, No. 1 was rebuilt and the stack raised to 65 feet; No. 2 was rebuilt in 1888 but retained its original dimensions. Both rebuilt stacks had closed tops and fronts and were equipped with double Player and Durham style pipe stoves. These changes, along with the introduction of sizable quantities of coke, increased the plant's total annual capacity to 37,000 tons by 1890. The addition of fire-brick stoves for No. 2 stack in 1896-97 increased the capacity further to 57,000 tons. Another rebuilding program on No. 2 stack, begun early in 1907, was suspended upon William H. Ainey's death on November 12, 1907. Work was never resumed; the whole plant was sold and entirely dismantled in 1908.

THE LEHIGH VALLEY IRON COMPANY

During the summer of 1853, veteran charcoal ironmaster Stephen Balliet organized the firm of Stephen Balliet & Company to build an anthracite furnace along the Lehigh. This firm, consisting of the senior Balliet and his sons, Aaron and Stephen Balliet, Jr., and his son-in-law, Benjamin S. Levan, purchased a parcel of land from Daniel Schreiber on the right bank of the river, just downstream from Schreiber's Ferry, for the furnace site. The foundation for No. 1 stack was laid and frame workers' houses were built in the autumn of 1853.

Stephen Balliet Sr.'s death in January 1854 led to the firm's reorganization and incorporation as the Lehigh Valley Iron Company with Joseph Laubach and Lewis A. Buckley admitted as partners. Joseph Laubach, a prominent businessman and politician, was elected president and Benjamin S. Levan, who had managed the Lehigh Furnace for his father-in-law since 1832, was appointed superintendent; both served until 1878. The first furnace had a 14 foot bosh and was originally 45 feet high; it was later raised to 60 feet. It was completed and blast applied in 1855; in 1857 it produced 4,465 tons of pig in 36 weeks. Early success led to the construction of No. 2 stack in 1862 and No. 3 in 1867-68; both were 55 feet high with a 16 foot bosh.

The Lehigh Valley Iron Company survived the first few years of the depression of the 1870s, but by December of 1878 debts had mounted to the point that the furnaces were blown out and bank-ruptcy declared. The firm was then taken over by the bankers. On June 18, 1878, it was reorganized as the Coplay Iron Company, Ltd. with Elisha P. Wilbur of Bethlehem as chairman and William H. Ainey of Allentown as secretary and treasurer. Valentine Weygandt Weaver, who earlier was employed by the Crane, the Thomas, and the Millerstown iron companies, and served as superintendent of the furnaces at Hokendauqua, Lock Ridge, and Macungie, became the first superintendent of the reorganized firm. Weaver remained superin-tendent until 1884, after which he was succeeded briefly by Harrison Bortz, who at the same time was also superintendent of the Lehigh Iron Company at Aineyville. Michael Fackenthal, previously secre-tary and superintendent of the Saucon Iron Company, then served as

145

View of the first furnace of the Lehigh Valley Iron Company, blown in during 1855.
Posing in front of the wagon is Valentine Weygandt Weaver, Jr., brother of the photographer, William Mickley Weaver. Their father was part owner and superintendent
of the works after it was reorganized as the Coplay Iron Company in 1878. Circa
1887. *Courtesy Elizabeth Weaver Moatz.*

The three furnaces of the Coplay Iron Company as they appeared in 1887. In the
foreground are furnaces Nos. 2 and 3; the old No. 1 is at the extreme right. As in
many other early furnaces, the pipe stoves were built adjacent to the furnace top.
Courtesy Elizabeth W. Moatz.

superintendent for a few years until succeeded in 1890 by Horace Boyd, who remained until the plant was liquidated.

The furnace plant, while modern enough when originally constructed, was never significantly updated. All three stacks were of masonry construction and had open tops and one old-style Cooper and two Thomas iron pipe stoves. Only No. 3 was ever remodeled; in 1889 it was rebuilt with a closed top to 70 by 15 feet. Simple cylindrical boilers generated steam for the three blowing engines. Steam-operated vertical elevators and manual filling barrows were used for charging. The stock houses for Nos. 2 and 3 stacks were conveniently located alongside the main line of the Lehigh Valley Railroad just below its junction with the Ironton Railroad. The annual capacity of the three stacks remained around 30,000 tons until some coke was mixed with the anthracite from the late 1880s on; this practice increased the capacity to approximately 34,000 tons. The product was principally foundry iron, branded "Coplay."

The exact date of the company's demise is unknown but is most likely around 1894 or 1895. No. 1 stack was abandoned in 1892; the 1898 Directory of the American Iron & Steel Association describes the plant as "Idle for several years and likely to remain long inactive. In the hands of the bondholders." Horace Boyd, the last superintendent, was reemployed as superintendent of the Thomas Iron Company's Saucon Furnaces on July 1, 1895. The site, just downstream from the Coplay-Northampton bridge, is now occupied by the lumber yard of the General Supply Company; no evidence of the furnaces remains.

THE LUCY FURNACE

The Lucy Furnace was situated at Glendon, between the canal and the Lehigh River, approximately midway between Chain Dam and the works of the Glendon Iron Company. The 65 by 16 foot stack was put into blast in 1872 by P. Uhler & Company. Financial difficulties soon led to its acquisition by Garrett B. Linderman, Elisha P. Wilbur and H. Green. The name was then changed to the Lucy Furnace in honor of Linderman's wife, Lucy Packer Linderman, the daughter of Asa Packer. Warren A. Wilbur, son of E.P. Wilbur and son-in-law of Linderman, was appointed superintendent. Between March 22, 1886, and December 15, 1887, the plant was leased by the Thomas Iron Company and managed by Fletcher Knight, superintendent of the nearby Keystone Furnace.

During the early 1890s, the Bethlehem Iron Company briefly leased the Lucy Furnace to supplement its own ironmaking capabilities which were then taxed to capacity because of its armaments contract. The furnace's original capacity was 10,000 tons per annum but the addition of a Kent double-brick stove and the introduction

1897 view of the engine house and ruins of Lucy Furnace, looking west. The engine house was still intact; less than two years later it had become a ruin. *Ronald Wynkoop Collection, Phillipsburg, N.J.*

Remains of the engine house at the Lucy Furnace in 1898. In the background are the works of the defunct Glendon Iron Company, which had not yet been demolished. *Canal Museum-Hugh Moore Park, Easton, Pa.*

of coke and richer Lake and foreign ores in the late 1880s increased it to 25,000 tons. The plant was abandoned and dismantled in 1897. Some ruins are still visible at the site, which is now part of the Hugh Moore Park.

THE MILLERSTOWN IRON COMPANY

The Millerstown Iron Company was organized in 1873 with James Weiler as president, F.S. Shimer as treasurer, and J.F.M. Shiffert as secretary. George D. Althouse of Philadelphia was hired as sales agent and Valentine W. Weaver was appointed superintendent. The furnace plant was built at Millerstown, renamed Macungie in 1876, and blown in on September 14, 1874. Most of the facilities were located in Lower Macungie Township at the eastern end of the property presently occupied by the Tyler Pipe Works (previously the East Penn Foundry Company).

The timing for the construction of the works was inopportune, for the panic of 1873 and the subsequent general depression resulted in greatly deflated iron prices. When the first shipment of iron was made on October 2, 1874, the price received for top grade iron, referred to as either No. 1x or Ax, was $28 per ton. By March 1875, when the furnace was blown out because of operating problems, the price had fallen to $25. After repairs were made the furnace was blown in again in June 1876, but by then the price had fallen to $22 per ton. This trend continued until November 1878, when it hit a low of $17 per ton for Ax iron, approximately $3 under the cost of production. The firm was unable to survive these conditions; the furnace was blown out in late April 1879, and bankruptcy declared.

A short time later, improvements in the iron market led to a reorganization, effective December 31, 1879, under the name of the Macungie Iron Company. William Mickley Weaver, the son of V.W. Weaver who had left the bankrupt firm to become superintendent of the reorganized Coplay Iron Company, was appointed superintendent, a position he held until his death in March, 1890. James Singmaster, the father-in-law of William M. Weaver and a prosperous merchant and land owner in Macungie, was president of the company from 1885 until his death on July 12, 1896.

The Macungie Iron Company was moderately successful until 1893, when economic conditions again forced it out of blast. The furnace then lay idle until 1899 when, after another sheriff's sale, it was acquired by the Empire Steel and Iron Company. The new owners put it into blast again on January 11, 1900. In 1902 it was shut down briefly for renovations and then operated profitably until 1910 when a dull iron market caused it to be blown out. In October 1912, after further renovations which included the installation of Durham pipe stoves, it was blown in again. On May 16, 1913, after a blast

149

The works of the Macungie Iron Company in the mid 1880s. The cast house is to the left of the boiler house stack, the engine house is to its right. The split rail fence is to discourage livestock from roaming onto the furnace property. *Courtesy Elizabeth Weaver Moatz.*

The boiler house of the Macungie Furnace was directly behind the stack, and the pipe stoves were directly behind the boiler house. Circa 1887. *Courtesy Elizabeth W. Moatz.*

150

Repairs were made to the boiler-house stack at the Macungie Furnace in 1887. *Courtesy Elizabeth W. Moatz.*

William Mickley Weaver, superintendent of the Macungie Iron Company from December 1879 until his death in 1890. Weaver was a superb amateur photographer who took all the photographs of the Macungie Furnace that appear in this book. Circa 1883. *Courtesy Elizabeth W. Moatz.*

Macungie Furnace. Stockpiles of surplus or off-grade pigs were common during the 1880s. *Courtesy Elizabeth W. Moatz.*

Cast house of the Macungie Furnace with pig beds prepared for the next cast. The refractory-coated "paddles" lying on the iron runner were used to direct the molten iron into the sow, from which it flowed into the individual pigs. Circa 1887. *Courtesy Elizabeth W. Moatz.*

Workers outside the Macungie Furnace stockhouse. The shovels were used to load the filling barrows. Circa 1887. *Courtesy Elizabeth W. Moatz.*

of only seven months, it was blown out. It was reactivated briefly in 1917-1918 in response to the national shortage of iron during the World War but was sold a few years later and the plant dismantled for scrap.

The Macungie Furnace was relatively modest by comparison with some of the other plants erected around the same time. The cylindrically shaped stack, fabricated from rolled iron boiler plate, had a 16 foot bosh but was only 56 feet high. It had no external bosh or hearth cooling system; the builders relied instead upon its thick refractory lining, the massive weight of which was supported by heavy cast iron columns, to contain the molten iron. As the firebrick in general use at that time was quickly eroded by the iron, plant shut-downs for relining the stack were commonplace. The blast was heated exclusively by the original old-pattern Kent stoves until 1910, when the Durham pipe stove was added. Its original capacity of 12,000 tons per year increased gradually with the introduction of coke and richer ores, and the installation of a second blowing engine, to a maximum of 25,000 tons.

OXFORD FURNACE

Like the Durham Furnace, ironmaking at Oxford, New Jersey, had its origins in colonial times. Located in what is now the north central portion of Warren County, Oxford Furnace was begun in 1741 by the Philadelphia merchant, Jonathan Robeson, on land that he leased from his neighbor, Joseph Shippen, Jr. Using local ores, the stone cold blast charcoal furnace was blown in during 1743. The products of this furnace were taken by road to the Delaware River at a site near the present town of Belvidere, where they were loaded on Durham Boats and taken to market.

By 1760, the furnace was owned by Dr. William Shippen, Sr. and Nicholas Biddle, although the actual iron production was under the supervision of ironmaster Jacob Starn. He was replaced by Joseph Shippen, the son of Dr. Shippen. During the American Revolution, the Oxford Furnace produced cannonballs and other munitions for the Continental Army. Toward the end of the eighteenth century, the furnace was leased to the partnership of Roberdeau, Showers and Campbell, who operated the works until 1806. In that year, Conrad Davis took over management of the furnace and he operated it successfully until 1809. In 1809, the Shippen estate sold the Oxford Furnace tract to Morris Robeson, grandson of the furnace's builder and the operator of the Martha and Weymouth furnaces in southern New Jersey. Morris Robeson was unsuccessful in his ironmaking efforts at Oxford. Due to a lack of charcoal for furnace fuel, Oxford went out of blast for over two decades.

The original charcoal-fueled Oxford Furnace as it appeared in the 1870s. The first documented American experiments with hot blast were conducted here in 1834 or 1835. The adjoining grist mill was later converted into a church. *Hugh Moore Historical Park and Museums, Inc., Easton, Pa.*

Cast house of the original Oxford Furnace in about 1890, a few years after it was blown out. *Hugh Moore Historical Park and Museums, Inc., Easton, Pa.*

Anthracite furnace at Oxford, New Jersey. From left to right are: cast house; furnace stack with charging elevator behind and iron pipe stoves in front, and downcomer leading from top of furnace to gas cleaner; gas cleaner; boiler stacks; engine house. Circa 1895. *Hugh Moore Historical Park and Museums, Inc., Easton, Pa.*

Blowing engine house at the Oxford Furnace. The long horizontal cylindrical structure is the cold blast receiver leading from the blowing engine to the stoves. *Hugh Moore Historical Park and Museums, Inc., Easton, Pa.*

By 1900 the pipe stoves were replaced with four regenerative stoves with a single masonry draft stack. Circa 1900. *Hugh Moore Historical Park and Museums, Inc., Easton, Pa.*

Ore roasters at the Oxford Furnace, circa 1900. Roasted magnetic ore was comparatively free from sulfur and was more easily reduced in the furnace. *Hugh Moore Historical Park and Museums, Inc., Easton, Pa.*

Morris Robeson died in 1824 and Oxford Furnace was inherited by his son, William P. Robeson, who soon sold a half interest in the works to his brother-in-law, John P.B. Maxwell. In 1832, the furnace was leased for ten years to the partnership of Henry, Jordan and Company. This partnership was composed of the noted Pennsylvania ironmaster William Henry, his brother-in-law John R. Wollee, and his nephew John Jordan, Jr. William Henry was a member of a noted family of gun manufacturers who operated a large manufacturing facility at Jacobsburg near Nazareth, Pennsylvania, and who also played prominent roles in affairs of the Moravian Church. In 1834, he hired Selden Scranton, the nephew of a merchant from Belvidere, New Jersey, to be his assistant at Oxford.

Henry planned to put the Oxford Furnace back in blast to supply iron for a forge that he operated at Analomink in what is now Monroe County, Pennsylvania. Heextensively improved the facilities at Oxford by rebuilding a portion of the stone furnace, erecting a new bridge between the stack house and the furnace, rebuilding the cast house, erecting a new charcoal barn, and constructing six workers' houses. He also installed new blowing machinery on the furnace and began experimenting with a primitive form of hot blast mechanism. On May 24, 1835, Oxford Furnace became the earliest documented iron furnace to employ hot blast techniques in America. In 1836, Henry modified his system so that the blast was heated by a pipe stove that was mounted at the tunnel head. This revised hot blast system was operated successfully until 1843.

In 1840, William Henry left Oxford to begin the development of an anthracite-fueled iron furnace at "Slocum's Hollow" in northeastern Pennsylvania. He was followed by Selden Scranton and his brother George in 1841. Oxford was placed under the management of Charles, a younger brother of George and Selden Scranton. In 1843, Henry abandoned the Pennsylvania enterprise, which was taken over by the George and Henry Scranton. By 1844, the iron furnace at Slocum's Hollow had become a success due to the infusions of capital by another Scranton brother, Joseph, and the building of a rolling mill to produce railroad rails. The town that grew up around this works was named Scranton in 1850.

Throughout the 1840s Charles Scranton remained in charge at Oxford and the works continued to prosper. In 1855, the Warren Railroad reached Oxford, greatly increasing access to raw materials and markets. Two years later, the Warren Railroad became a part of the Delaware, Lackawanna and Western system; in that year the Oxford Furnace produced 906 tons of iron, which was shipped to market via this line. In 1859, Selden Scranton returned to Oxford to assume control of the plant, described by Lesley's Iron Manufacturers Guide as possessing a "steam hot blast charcoal and anthracite furnace, 8 ft. diameter bosh, 38 ft. high runs 2/3 year on charcoal and 1/3 year on anthracite."

In 1863, the company was reorganized as S.T. Scranton and Company; a rolling mill and a nail factory were completed two years later. In 1866, the production facilities as Oxford were further expanded with the construction of a modern anthracite-fueled sheet iron furnace designated as Furnace No. 2 at a site west of the present Washington Avenue. A profitable business was also developed during this period, casting car wheels for the Delaware, Lackawanna and Western Railroad. In 1871, Furnace No. 2 was rebuilt to be 63 feet high and 18 feet in diameter at the bosh.

The prosperity at Oxford vanished rapidly after the panic of 1873. Selden Scranton was bankrupted that year and the facilities at Oxford seized by the Delaware, Lackawanna and Western, which reorganized the works as the Oxford Iron and Nail Company in 1882. In 1884, the original charcoal fueled Furnace No. 1 was permanently blown out. Furnace No. 2, the rolling mill, and the rail factory continued to be operated until 1895 when the general depression of the iron industry forced the shutdown of almost all of these facilities.

The Empire Iron and Steel Company purchased the assets of the Oxford Iron and Nail Company in 1900. Concentrating on the operation of Furnace No. 2, Empire sold the rolling mill to the Jensen Brothers Company which dismantled it and later re-erected it in Columbia, Pennsylvania.

In 1910, Furnace No. 2 became the site of a pioneering technological innovation, when America's first turbo blower was installed there as an experiment by the General Electric Corporation. It replaced two I.P. Morris blowing engines that had been originally installed at the Glendon Iron Company in 1893. In 1899 these engines were salvaged by the Empire Steel and Iron Company which used them until 1905 in their Allentown works. Moved to Oxford in 1908, these engines could not be made to run properly there. The turbo blower that replaced them had a capacity of 22,500 cubic feet of air per minute, at 1500 revolutions per minute. It was an immediate success and became the direct ancestor of almost all modern industrial turbo-blower and airplane and automobile engine turbocharger installations.

Empire Steel and Iron Company operated Furnace No. 2 until 1921 when it was permanently blown out due to the post-World War I business recession.

The modern town of Oxford, New Jersey, has many remains of its iron history. Although almost no trace remains of Furnace No. 2, Furnace No. 1 survives as a stabilized ruin as does the intact former ironmaster's mansion that is commonly called the Shippen Manor

House. It is owned by Warren County, New Jersey, which plans to restore it as a cultural center. The former car-wheel foundry and the former dwelling places of several members of the Scranton family are still also extant. Oxford also contains several intact neighborhoods of late nineteenth-century workers' houses.

THE NORTHAMPTON IRON COMPANY

The furnace of the Northampton Iron Company was built near Shimersville, Lower Saucon Township, in 1873. It occupied a site at the mouth of the Saucon Creek between the Lehigh River and the Lehigh Valley Railroad, about a quarter mile upstream from the Freemansburg depot. The 64 by 16 foot stack, blown in on July 17, 1873, had an annual capacity of slightly more than 11,000 tons. Around 1880 the plant was leased to the Bethlehem Iron Company which operated it through the 1880s. The lease was terminated in the early 1890s and the firm, then headed by Warren A. Wilbur as president and R.M. Gummere as secretary-treasurer, advertised for a new lessee. As none could be found, the plant lay idle until dismantled in 1898.

THE NORTH PENN IRON COMPANY

The single stack of the North Penn Iron Company was built at Bingen, Lower Saucon Township, in 1870. It was located adjacent to the Bingen depot of the North Penn Railroad, between the railroad and Saucon Creek. The sheet-iron stack was 65 feet high; its bosh, originally 18 feet in diameter, was later reduced first to 17 feet and then to 16 feet. Most of the ore used came from the Gangewere beds and company-operated mines in both Upper and Lower Saucon townships. Limestone was obtained from quarries within a few hundred yards of the plant. The company experienced both operating and economic difficulties during the 1870s and around 1880 the furnace was purchased by the Bethlehem Iron Company and designated No. 7 stack. It was operated by Bethlehem until 1897, when it was blown out and dismantled. Later the slag dump was quarried away and the site graded. Nothing remains to be seen.

PEQUEST FURNACE

In 1874, the Pequest Mining and Manufacturing Company, controlled by local Warren County and Lehigh Valley entrepreneurs, began construction of an anthracite-fueled sheet-iron stack on a tract of land two miles to the north of Oxford, New Jersey. The furnace was 58 feet high and 16 feet in diameter at the bosh, with a closed top and steam-driven blowing engines. It was blown in on October 27, 1874.

1905 view of Pequest Furnace looking north. The building on the right is the stockhouse and behind it is the elevator and furnace. *Courtesy Michael S. King Collection.*

By 1877, Pequest Furnace had an annual production of 8,000 tons of iron made from magnetite ore that was mined on the company's property. Almost all of the iron produced there was converted into nails at a rolling mill on the site. Only a small amount of pig iron was sold on the open market. The company shipped its products to market via the adjacent Delaware, Lackawanna and Western Railroad.

E.J. Saeger of Allentown, Pennsylvania, served as the president of the Pequest Mining and Manufacturing Company until the plant was sold to the firm of Cooper and Hewitt in 1879. The rolling mill was shut down, and the Pequest Furnace began producing foundry and gray forge pig iron at an annual rate of 14,000 tons. The local ores were supplemented by a combination of higher grade ores from the Cooper and Hewitt's other New Jersey properties, such as the Charlotteburg, Green Ponds, Peters Hibernia, Pitney and Cannon mines. A total of 500 tons of iron ore was consumed at the furnace each week.

161

One railcar filled with limestone for furnace flux was shipped daily to the Pequest Furnace from Franklin in adjacent Sussex County. By the end of 1880, Pequest Furnace was producing approximately 50 tons of iron per day, but since it proved to be very expensive to operate Cooper and Hewitt decided to cut costs by combining Pequest's administration with that of their large Durham Furnace in Pennsylvania. However, this measure did not produce the desired economies and by 1886, Cooper and Hewitt had suffered a total loss of $100,000 at Pequest Furnace.

In 1884, the Pequest Furnace was rebuilt by Cooper and Hewitt. When this rebuilding work was completed, it was 67½ feet high and 16½ feet wide at the bosh. The blast was heated by Durham stoves. Connellsville coke was introduced to supplement anthracite as a furnace fuel, with each charge utilizing preparations of 1/8 coke and 7/8 anthracite. The rebuilt Pequest Furnace produced foundry, grey forge, and Bessemer pig iron, the latter for use in steel mills. In 1888, the furnace produced 27,845 tons of iron. Despite it's improved productivity, Cooper and Hewitt could not make a profit from this facility and, in 1893, they shut it down.

In 1899, Cooper and Hewitt leased the Pequest Furnace to Joseph Wharton, the Philadelphia entrepreneur who was a major stockholder in the Bethlehem Iron Company and who owned and operated extensive iron properties in New Jersey, including a nearby furnace complex at Hackettstown. However, Wharton was not successful in his operations at Pequest and it was soon returned to the management of Cooper and Hewitt. In 1908, the Pequest Furnace produced 25,000 tons of iron utilizing a mixture of ½ Connellsville coke and ½ anthracite as furnace fuel. By 1910, Pequest Furnace had been shut permanently. It was demolished during the next decade.

THE SAUCON IRON COMPANY

The Saucon Iron Company was chartered on August 21, 1866, with George W. Whitaker as president, Jacob Riegel as treasurer and Andrew R. Whitaker as secretary. The board of directors was composed almost entirely of the major stockholders, the largest of which were Joseph Wharton with 300 shares and Jacob Riegel with 275 shares. The stock was valued at $100 per share. Michael Fackenthal, brother of B.F. Fackenthal, Jr., embarked upon his own career at this plant, starting as head book-keeper in 1869. In 1873 he was promoted to secretary and in 1877 to superintendent, a position he held until moving to the Coplay Iron Company in 1885.

The furnace lay between the tracks of the North Penn Railroad and the Saucon Creek, just north of the original boundary of the borough of Hellertown. Construction commenced soon after the company was chartered. No. 1 stack was blown in on March 25, 1868, and

No. 2 was put into blast on May 25, 1870. As the organizers were principally merchants and financiers, not ironmasters, they contracted the design of the plant to John M. Hartman, the first engineer in this country to make blast-furnace design a specialty. Both stacks were fabricated from heavy iron plates and had a thick refractory lining supported by cast iron posts. This design, similar to that used on the first furnace built by the Bethlehem Iron Company a few years earlier, represented a great improvement over the traditional masonry stacks. It permitted greater access to the work area around the hearth and allowed for more uniform tuyere placement. Both stacks had 16-foot boshes; No. 1 was 50 feet high and No. 2 was 60 feet high.

Despite the comparatively modern design of the plant, the company had difficulty surviving the "dull times" following the panic of 1873. It limped along, out of blast as often as it was in, until November 5, 1884, when the stockholders finally agreed to sell out to the Thomas Iron Company for $300,000. The sale price was established by Joseph Wharton, who offered to buy the plant himself for $300,000, "but would not stand in the way of the Thomas Iron Company if they made the same offer." The sale was consummated on December 13, 1884, and stacks No. 1 and No. 2 were redesignated No. 10 and No. 11 of the Thomas Iron Company.

After the takeover Horace Boyd was appointed superintendent and the furnaces were put back into blast. When Boyd left in 1890 to serve as superintendent of the Coplay Iron Company, he was replaced by Lee S. Clymer, who supervised the modernization program undertaken in 1893-1894. The original pipe stoves were replaced with Durham-style stoves and No. 10 stack was raised to 75 feet. These improvements, along with the introduction of greater quantities of coke, raised the plant's capacity from 25,000 to 55,000 tons. To accommodate the increased production, a Hartman pig-casting machine was installed, thereby eliminating the need for expanding the cast houses. The original blowing engines, housed in a massive stone-arch structure each with its own boiler plant on top, remained the only source of blast until 1916 when a more powerful, though secondhand, engine was installed to raise the pressure and volume of the blast.

The ores used originally consisted primarily of local Saucon Valley limonite, the bulk of which came from the Wharton and the Koch mines east of Hellertown, and New Jersey magnetite. After the turn of the century, Lake and foreign ores were commonly used as well. Dolomitic limestone flux was obtained from the Wagner, Riegel and Grim quarries along the Saucon Creek and transported to the furnace by the North Penn Railroad and by short company-operated spurs. By 1917 the use of anthracite was discontinued completely

163

and the furnaces operated exclusively on beehive and by-product coke.

In 1918 No. 11 stack was rebuilt to 72 by 16 feet and the use of No. 10, which required a reline, was discontinued. The rebuilt No. 11 stack, rated at 42,000 tons per annum, remained in use until late 1921. Soon thereafter the whole plant was sold and dismantled for scrap. The massive stone arches of the engine house remained standing until the mid 1960s when they were declared a safety hazard and the owner, the Bethlehem Steel Corporation, was compelled to knock them down. In 1974 the property was sold to the City of Bethlehem and the Borough of Hellertown. Only the concrete trestle piers and the extensive slag dump remain to remind occasional visitors of the site's former activities.

The two stacks of the Saucon works of the Thomas Iron Company, as they appeared early this century. The Durham pipe stoves in the left foreground were added in the modernization program of 1893-1894. The tracks of the North Penn Branch of the Philadelphia & Reading Railroad are in the foreground. *From the 1904 stockholders report of the Thomas Iron Company.*

The workers of the Saucon Iron Company were originally nearly all local Pennsylvania
Germans. By the turn of the century many other nationalities were represented.
Courtesy Richard Kantor.

The cast houses of the Saucon works around 1903, as pictured in the 1904 stockholders report. The twin engine houses, each with its own boiler plant on top, sit
between the two furnace stacks.

Stacks Nos. 1 and 2 of the Thomas Iron Company under construction in late 1854 or early 1855. The blowing engines were housed behind the arch-window structure between the two stacks. *Courtesy American Iron and Steel Institute.*

Thomas Iron Company works as they appeared at the turn of the century. Dam No. 6 of the Lehigh Navigation Company is in the foreground. *From the 1904 stockholders report.*

THE THOMAS IRON COMPANY

The anthracite iron boom was well under way when the founders of the Thomas Iron Company first met in Mr. White's tavern in Center Square, Easton, on February 14, 1854. Of the eighteen gentlemen who attended this first organizational meeting, all but one subsequently became subscribers to the capital stock of the company. The founders were men of considerable talent who had already achieved distinction and financial success in other spheres of endeavor; most were interested in investing in the iron industry simply to increase their fortunes. The majority were businessmen and professionals from Easton and Bethlehem; a few were from outside the Lehigh Valley. Very little was accomplished at the first organizational meeting except to "name the Company in honor of David Thomas, who projected the Company, and in recognition of his work, the pioneer in the successful manufacture of anthracite iron" and to fix the capital at $200,000.

During the course of the next few months, additional organizational meetings were held and an earlier decision to organize as "general partners" was abandoned when a special charter from the State of Pennsylvania was granted and approved on April 4, 1854. This charter remained in effect for the next 84 years before it was finally surrendered in June, 1942, nearly 15 years after the last furnace was in blast. The first board of directors included E.A. Douglas, William H. Talcott, Ephraim Marsh, Peter S. Michler, John Drake, Samuel S. Chidsey and C.A. Luckenbach. David Thomas was made trustee of real estate and his son Samuel was appointed superintendent.

Though only 27 at the time of his appointment, Samuel Thomas was certainly well qualified for the position. From the age of 16 he had worked for his father at the Lehigh Crane Iron Works. Then, early in 1848, at the age of just 21, he was sent to Boonton, New Jersey, where he supervised the construction of and successfully blew in an anthracite furnace for the Boonton Iron Works. Later in the same year he returned to Catasauqua to assist his father in the construction of No. 4 and No. 5 furnaces. Samuel Thomas was destined to become one of the leading figures in the Thomas Iron Company, serving first as superintendent and then appointed a director and elected president on August 31, 1864. He continued as president for the next 23 years, finally resigning the office on September 22, 1887, so that he might fulfill his long-held ambition to build a modern iron works in Alabama. He remained a director of the Thomas Iron Company until his death at Catasauqua on February 21, 1906. Like most ventures undertaken by Samuel Thomas, the works built at Thomas, Alabama, were a success. When he retired from all active management in 1899, all Thomas-owned properties in

167

Alabama were sold to the Republic Iron and Steel Company. The furnaces which he constructed there in 1887 were sufficiently modern that the Republic Steel Company (now part of LTV Corp.) continued them in operation, producing merchant pig until October 28, 1972, when the last cast was made from a Thomas-built furnace.

For the site of their furnace plant, the organizers of the Thomas Iron Company authorized David Thomas to buy the Thomas Butz farm, situated on the right bank of the Lehigh River about one mile upstream from Catasauqua. The company town subsequently laid out became the nucleus of present-day Hokendauqua. A contract for all the mason and bricklaying work was awarded to Samuel McHose of Allentown. The blowing engines, like those used in most Thomas-built furnaces, were among the largest available at the time, having steam cylinders 56 inches in diameter and blowing cylinders 84 inches in diameter with 9-foot stroke. Furnace No. 1 was quickly constructed and blown in on June 3, 1855; No. 2 furnace was put into blast on October 27, 1855.

Soon after completing construction of its first two furnaces, the Thomas Iron Company purchased, in 1856, the Richard Mine near Mount Hope, New Jersey. This highly productive mine contained large deposits of high-grade magnetic ores that were used in the Thomas furnaces. By 1891 the mine had become the largest producer of iron ore in New Jersey, supplying over 84,000 tons in that year alone. The company continued to operate the Richard Mine until 1923, when it sold the property to the Philadelphia and Reading Coal and Iron Company.

The first two furnaces of the Thomas works were considered models for other ironmakers to emulate and were chosen by the noted English metallurgist, Dr. John Percy, as the example to illustrate the part of his pioneering metallurgical text that dealt with American anthracite ironmaking. In commenting on this industry, he made the following observations:

> But the principal manufacture must always cling to the Lehigh, Schuylkill and Lower Susquehanna valleys, in Pennsylvania, where ore is abundant, the coal near at hand, and the flux on the spot; where the whole land is a garden, and, therefore, food cheap and plentiful, and the great sea-ports not far off. For all these considerations, as well as for beauty, size, and convenience of build, and for its historic interest, the Thomas furnaces, which have been selected as illustrative of the American manufacture for this work, stand pre-eminent.

Other contemporary commentators likewise considered the Thomas works among the finest in America. Professor J.P. Lesley attributed their success primarily to the capable management of David and Samuel Thomas:

> The consummate skill and long experience of the manager must no doubt avoid or redress the ordinary troubles of the process, but this immense production even from these first class stacks can be accounted for only by the enormous consumption of oxygen which they are allowed. It is a satisfactory evidence of the constancy and reliability of the chemical and mechanical laws at our command for making iron that the introducer and oldest producer of anthracite iron in America has not been superseded, but is still able to lead off the greatly enhanced production with these high figures. It is evidently no game of chance, but a trial of practical wisdom based on experience and insured by the improvement of all the means at the disposal of man. In a word here stands the demonstration that a large and well built crucible, properly stocked with good ores and properly blown with power to spare, must be a great and continued success.

In 1857, No. 1 stack produced 9,731 tons of iron and No. 2 produced 8,366 tons, far more than the average furnace of that day. Later, four more furnaces were added to the Hokendauqua plant, No. 3 blown in on July 18, 1862, No. 4 on April 29, 1863, No. 5 on September 15, 1873, and No. 6 on January 19, 1874. Later acquisitions increased the number of furnaces operated by the Thomas Iron Company to eleven and, for a brief time, twelve. The Lock Ridge Iron Company was acquired on May 1, 1869; the Keystone Furnace, chartered as D. Runkle Company, was purchased by April 1, 1882 and the works of the Saucon Iron Company were purchased on December 13, 1884. The Lucy Furnace was operated under lease from March 22, 1886, until December 15, 1887.

All of the original Hokendauqua furnaces, including those built in the 1870s, were traditional masonry stacks and employed iron pipe stoves. It was not until the early 1890s that any significant improvements were made to the works. In 1891 three regenerative stoves, 65 by 17 feet, were added to No. 6 stack. The old No. 1 stack was demolished after its last blast on February 7, 1893, and replaced with a new sheet iron stack, 80 by 17 feet, which was blown in on August 1, 1894. This furnace was operated with Durham pipe stoves until January 8, 1898, when it was equipped with three Taws and Hartman regenerative stoves, all 80 by 17 feet. The old No. 3 stack was blown out on October 26, 1897, and replaced with a new sheet-iron stack similar to the rebuilt No. 1. The new No. 3, equipped with three regenerative stoves which were duplicates of those added to No. 1, was put into blast on October 26, 1899. No. 2

The Hokendauqua works in March, 1880. Furnaces 3 and 4, and 5 and 6 were built in pairs and were virtual duplicates of the original stacks. *From the 1904 stockholders report.*

W. P. HARDENBERGH   J. SAMUEL KRAUSE   J. S. RODENBAUGH   FRED R. DRAKE   JAMES W. WEAVER Secy. & Treas.
        SAMUEL THOMAS   B. F. FACKENTHAL, Jr.   WILLIAM H HULICK
                                            President   Vice-President
BOARD OF DIRECTORS AND TREASURER OF THE THOMAS IRON COMPANY, February 28, 1904.

Benjamin Franklin Fackenthal, Jr., president from 1893 until 1913, served as a consultant to the ironmaking and mining industries for nearly 40 years after his resignation. A founder of the Bucks County Historical Society, he was the foremost historian of ironmaking in eastern Pennsylvania. James W. Weaver, the son of Valentine W. Weaver and nephew of Samuel Thomas, entered the employ of the company in 1867. He ended his 48-year career in 1915, when he was secretary and treasurer of the company.

170

The new engine house of the Thomas works is in the foreground. Furnace No. 1, rebuilt in 1894 as a sheet-iron stack and still charged with a vertical elevator, is on the right. *Courtesy Randolph L. Kulp.*

View of the Hokendauqua works as they appeared around 1930. The Lehigh Coal and Navigation Company's No. 6 dam and guard lock are in the foreground. The railroad tracks are those of the Central Railroad of New Jersey. The sole remaining stack, the skip-charged Mary Furnace, is in the right background. *Pennsylvania Canal Society Collection, Canal Museum, Easton, Pa.*

furnace was abandoned on August 13, 1893, and No. 4 was abandoned after its last blast on May 20, 1902.

During 1905 two new Allis-Chalmers cross-compound blowing engines were added to stacks 1 and 3, and in 1906 a fourth regenerative stove was added to each of these stacks. No. 5 stack, which had been abandoned in 1897, was revived in 1899 and in 1903 was equipped with Durham pipe stoves. By 1915, No. 5 and No. 6, both old stone stacks, had been abandoned. The two remaining stacks, No. 1 and No. 3, were continually updated through the early 1920s. Additional, and larger, regenerative stoves were added and a Pittsburgh Coal Washer Company double-strand pig-casting machine was installed. By 1924 No. 1 stack had been abandoned and in 1927 No. 3 stack, which had been renamed the Mary Furnace, was also blown out. The works were sold in the mid 1930s to the Bethlehem Steel Company which dismantled the entire plant for scrap.

During its last few years the Thomas Works were operated by the Reading Iron Company. The successors of B.F. Fackenthal, Jr., who had served as president from January 19, 1893, until May 1, 1913, were unable to lead the company through the post-war depression. Ralph H. Sweetser, who served as president from August 1, 1913, until July 1, 1916, made an abortive and costly effort to reopen some of the company's local limonite mines. Some of his modernization programs also yielded a poor return on the investments. Sweetser's successor, William A. Barrows, Jr., finally arranged to sell the company's stock to Drexel & Company on June 30, 1922. Drexel & Company subsequently sold the railroad stocks to the Reading, Lehigh Valley, and New Jersey Central railroads and the other plants and assets to the Reading Iron Company. The Alburtis and the Hellertown properties were sold off and the Hokendauqua works operated as a subsidiary until the last furnace was blown out.

CHAPTER VI

THE BETHLEHEM IRON (STEEL) COMPANY

The evolution of the Bethlehem Iron Company differed in several important ways from the development of the other anthracite iron companies of the Lehigh Valley. Unlike almost all of the other iron producers in this region, which continued to concentrate on the smelting of merchant pig iron for the open market, the Bethlehem Iron Company had been founded to produce a particular finished product--wrought iron railroad rails. It alone possessed sufficient capital resources and technological expertise to become a steel maker. Its management exhibited an adaptability and forethought that enabled the Bethlehem Iron Company to develop new products as market conditions in the iron and steel industry changed rapidly during the last decades of the nineteenth century. In the process of developing these new products, the Bethlehem Iron Company had a dramatic and lasting impact on the early stages of the American military-industrial complex.

The initial development of the Bethlehem Iron Company was directed by Augustus Wolle, a merchant from Bethlehem. A member of an old and prominent Moravian family, Wolle had been one of the original backers of the Thomas Iron Company in 1854. Since this investment quickly proved to be profitable, Wolle looked for other opportunities in the Lehigh Valley's burgeoning iron industry. By 1857 he had leased the Gangewere iron ore deposits in Lower Saucon Township and obtained a charter for a new enterprise, the Saucona Iron Company, to exploit them.

Wolle planned to develop the Saucona Iron Company as a merchant pig iron producer similar to the Thomas Iron Company and the other blast furnaces that were operating at that time. However, before any facilities could be constructed, the Saucona Iron Company's destiny was forever altered by the intervention of new and much more powerful entrepreneurs, the management of the Lehigh Valley Railroad. Although the ultimate financial power was held by Asa Packer, the Lehigh Valley Railroad's principal stockholder, the actual involvement of the Lehigh Valley Railroad in Wolle's nascent iron company was directed by Robert H. Sayre, the line's Chief Engineer and General Superintendent. It was Sayre who had recently moved the operating headquarters of the Lehigh Valley Railroad from Mauch Chunk to the new community which would soon evolve into the Borough of South Bethlehem. As his diaries reveal, Sayre saw in Wolle's enterprise an opportunity for the Lehigh Valley Railroad to

1860 photographic portrait of John Fritz (1822-1913) soon after his arrival to superintend the construction of the Bethlehem plant. His mechanical genius would place the Bethlehem Iron Company in the forefront of iron- and steelmaking technology for the remainder of the nineteenth century. *John Fritz Collection, Hugh Moore Historical Park and Museums, Inc., Easton, Pa.*

1868 portrait of Robert H. Sayre (1824-1907), the dominant figure in the development of the Lehigh Valley Railroad. While serving as chief engineer and superintendent of the railroad, he used its capital to underwrite the creation of the Bethlehem Iron Company. He became general manager of Bethlehem Iron in 1885, and continued to serve the company until he retired in 1899. He and John Fritz deserve much of the credit for the company's success. *Robert H. Sayre Collection, Hugh Moore Historical Park and Museums, Inc., Easton, Pa.*

develop a badly needed captive, and profitable, source of high quality wrought iron rails.

Up to this point, the Lehigh Valley Railroad had been purchasing all of its rails from British suppliers or from the Lackawanna Iron and Coal Company at Scranton, Pennsylvania. However, each of these sources of rail had significant disadvantages. British rails were expensive and Lackawanna rails, although cheaper, were far from uniform in quality. And, since the Scranton rail mill was controlled by the managers of the competing Delaware, Lackawanna and Western Railroad, Sayre was reluctant to subsidize the rival line through the continued purchase of Lackawanna rails. As a result, Sayre envisioned Wolle's paper company as the basis for the development of a rail mill that would not only meet the Lehigh Valley Railroad's needs, but would also generate profits through the sale of its products to other lines. The Saucona Iron Company was therefore reorganized as the Bethlehem Rolling Mill and Iron Company, in 1860, in order to better reflect its intended function.

Under the direction of Sayre and the other members of the Lehigh Valley Railroad management, the location of the reorganized enterprise's future plant was moved from the Saucon Valley to a strategically located parcel of land along the south bank of the Lehigh River in South Bethlehem, adjacent to the junction of the Lehigh Valley and North Penn railroads. Not only would this new plant site facilitate the delivery of such needed raw materials as anthracite coal and iron ore, but it would also allow easy shipment via the Lehigh Valley Railroad and its connecting lines to New York, and also via the North Penn Railroad to Philadelphia.

Determined to produce the highest quality rails at the lowest possible cost, Robert H. Sayre decided to hire John Fritz to design, construct, and oversee the operation of the firm's production facilities. This decision was to have profound consequences for the future development of the Bethlehem Rolling Mill and Iron Company, because John Fritz was a mechanical genius of the highest order who had recently patented a revolutionary machine for the production of wrought iron railroad rails.

As superintendent of the Cambria Iron Company at Johnstown, Pennsylvania, John Fritz had developed a "three high" rail mill which solved many of the problems that had long been associated with rail production in America. In conventional "two high" mills, the hot iron blooms could not be completely rolled into rails in a single operation, because they had to be dragged back to the front of the mill after each pass through the rolls. The blooms often cooled during the process and would crack or shatter as they were reinserted between the rolls for another pass. To prevent such damage, Fritz redesigned Cambria's rail mill as a "three high" unit

176

that enabled heated blooms to be passed rapidly back and forth so they could be completely converted into rails before they had a chance to cool and crack.

The three high rail mill at Cambria began operation on July 29, 1857, and it proved to be an immediate success. For the first time in America, it was possible to produce large quantities of uniformly high quality rails at a reasonable cost. Since John Fritz had, on October 5, 1858, obtained a patent for his three high mill, he was able to control the use of his invention. At the same time, he was becoming increasingly disenchanted with his position at Johnstown.

The surviving personal papers of John Fritz, which recently became available and are stored at the archives of the Hugh Moore Historical Park and Museums in Easton, Pennsylvania, shed new light on John Fritz's reasons for leaving Johnstown.

It is known from John Fritz's Autobiography that he had become discontented as a result of constant opposition from the directors of the Cambria Iron Company to his mechanical innovations. A man of genuis, he had begun to feel stifled. However, an even larger factor in his desire to leave Johnstown was concern for his family's future. As we have now learned from his letters, he had come to regard Johnstown as an unhealthy place. While Johnstown remained a raw industrial frontier community offering little in the way of amenities for his family, Bethlehem, in contrast, was a long-established community with fine schools and a rich cultural life. Since it was located near the center of America's most productive iron-making region, it would give John Fritz a great opportunity to display his talents.

All of these factors were addressed in a masterful letter of May 1, 1860, from Sayre to Fritz that shows both Robert H. Sayre's great insight into human nature and his unbounded optimism for the future of the Lehigh Valley"

I can fully appreciate the objections that would natu-
rally arise to your leaving an establishment that you have
become so thoroughly identified with, at the same time if
the country does not suit you or your family and you can
change to a location that will suit you without suffering
pecuniarily and with a prospect of adding to instead of
detracting from your reputation as an ironmaster, I think
you are justifiable in making the change. You say truly
that a man's merit is measured by his success. You will
also bear in mind that the more generally a man's success
is known to the public, the faster and higher he will raise
in public favor. You can leave Johnstown in complete and
thorough order mechanically and I presume all right finan-
cially. The establishment of a good mill at this place

[South Bethlehem] producing a first rate quality of rails will establish your reputation in a section of the country this is destined to be in my opinion the most populous and wealthy in this or any other state. When I see the rapid strides that business has taken in this Valley for the past 10 years and think of the impetus that the improvements now in contemplation will give to it in the next 10, I predict a future for it that will surprise its most sanguine citizens. To make our growth healthy we must have no failures hence my desire to have the Bethlehem Mill start upon a good basis . . . In regard to your having entire control of the establishment, I tell them [the other investors] that a rolling mill is like a man of war, it must have one Captain. I do not apprehend any difficulty in the way of everything moving along pleasantly. Hoping to have the pleasure of seeing you soon and hearing you say that you are coming to dwell among us.

By June 1860, John Fritz had made his decision to leave Johnstown and accept the position as Superintendent of the Bethlehem Rolling Mill and Iron Company. The final element that brought about this move may well have been the terms of the contract offered to him. Arriving at Bethlehem on July 5, his contract with his new employers was ratified two days later by a resolution of the Board of Directors. The key provision of this contract, a portion of which is reproduced below, was his ability to gain equity in the new concern. The importance of John Fritz's patent on the three high rail mill is also quite evident from this document. This patent may have been the inducement that led the Company to offer him such a generous remuneration.

Resolved that we appoint John Fritz of Johnstown, Pa., General Manager and Superintendent of the Works of the Company both during the construction of the same and when in operation at a salary of five thousand dollars per annum, the same commencing on the first of July, 1860, and in addition thereto to pay him a bonus of forty shares of the capital stock of the Company on the first of July, 1861, and furthermore twenty shares on the first day of July, 1862, and twenty shares on the first of July, 1863, and again twenty shares on the first of July, 1864. The said John Fritz giving the Company the use of his patent for the three high rolls for their mill or mills free of charge.

With the promise of financial security and assurances of management independence, Fritz began the task of designing and supervising the production facilities of the Bethlehem Rolling Mill and Iron Company. On July 16, 1860, ground was broken for a plant that would contain two blast furnaces and a rolling mill complex with eight double puddling furnaces (for the conversion of the pig iron from the blast furnace into wrought iron for rail production), six heating furnaces, and an improved three high rail mill.

Fritz specified high standards for the machinery, most of which was produced (according to letters that are contained in his papers) by the Orchard Iron Works at Pottsville, Pennsylvania, and the firm of Matthews and Moore at the Bush Hill Iron Works of Philadelphia. The buildings of the new plant were constructed from local stone and roofed with slate.

Although the political and economic uncertainty caused by the election of Abraham Lincoln as president and the accompanying threat of Southern secession caused a slowdown in plant construction during the spring of 1860-1861, Sayre and the other members of the Lehigh Valley Railroad management continued to support the enterprise. According to both John Fritz's surviving notebooks and Robert Sayre's personal diaries, Fritz and Sayre visited almost all of the major iron furnaces in the Lehigh Valley, in northeastern Pennsylvania, and in northern New Jersey during this period to examine contemporary ironmaking and rolling technology. The company was greatly hindered by damage caused by a flood on June 4, 1862, which washed away a portion of the fill on which the rail mill was being constructed. After repairing the flood damage, work proceeded on completing the works.

Reorganized as the Bethlehem Iron Company, the young corporation continued to develop. On January 4, 1863, the first cast was made from the Bethlehem Iron Company's No. 1 Furnace. No. 1 furnace was technological breakthrough because it was of iron shell construction, the first of this type to be built in the Lehigh Valley. The entire stack was built from quarter-inch-thick iron boiler plate; it was lined with refractory brick 62 feet high, and had a 16-foot-diameter bosh. It soon proved to be much more productive than the traditional stone furnaces of the other iron companies in the Lehigh Valley. On July 27, the puddling furnaces began producing wrought iron blooms for the rail rolling mill. The first rails were rolled in September, and Bethlehem Iron Company rails quickly gained a reputation for excellence. These rails also had a ready market since the Lehigh Valley Railroad purchased almost all of the initial production. The Central Railroad of New Jersey, whose president John Taylor Johnston was a member of the Bethlehem Iron Company's Board of Directors, also became a major customer. By the end of 1863, the works of the Bethlehem Iron Company had grown to include four stationary steam engines, one blast furnace, 14 puddling furnaces, nine heating furnaces, a 21- inch (based on the diameter of the rolls) puddle train and a 21-inch rail train.

The Bethlehem Iron Company's second blast furnace was completed in 1867. In his **Autobiography**, John Fritz referred to it as being of an unusual "crinoline" design due to its supposed resemblance to the fashionable ladies' skirts of that time. Instead of using boiler plate, it was constructed with 7/8-inch-thick by 8-inch-wide wrought iron bands which were riveted to 8½-inch wrought-iron uprights on 30-inch centers. Small viewing holes at various locations allowed the operators to inspect the furnace for malfunctions.

During this same period John Fritz also supervised the construction of a large machine shop and foundry complex, the products of which greatly expanded the Company's markets. In 1868, the Bethlehem Iron Company completed Furnace No. 3. Located in an outlying area of the works, it was 50 feet in height and 13 feet in diameter at the bosh.

The pervasive influence of the management of the Lehigh Valley Railroad continued to guide the company's growth. Under Robert H. Sayre's direction, the railroad ran special trains to bring executives from various eastern railroads to view the Bethlehem Iron Company's plant and products. Sayre recorded in his diaries that these trains became an effective marketing tool.

The management of the Lehigh Valley Railroad, and Sayre in particular, convinced Fritz that the Bethlehem Iron Company should begin to manufacture steel. The decision to pursue this course of action may have been the crucial point in the company's history, the one that would ultimately ensure its survival until the present day.

The impetus for Sayre's decision to begin steel production at Bethlehem was provided by the growing need of the Lehigh Valley Railroad for steel rails. Although John Fritz's invention of the three high mill had broken British dominance of the American rail market by making it possible to produce large quantities of superior wrought iron rails at a reasonable cost, the invention of the Bessemer or pneumatic process of steel production had once again given British ironworks a technological edge. Developed by Henry Bessemer during the 1850s, the pneumatic process involved introducing a blast of air into a furnace vessel that contained molten pig iron. This blast of air caused the carbon in the pig iron to be partially burned off, thus producing steel. By the early 1860s British manufacturers were producing Bessemer steel rails which had almost four times the resistance to wear as the best American wrought iron rails. Although they were expensive, demand for steel rails grew rapidly in the United States. According to figures that are cited by Jeanne McHugh in her work, <u>Alexander Holley and the Makers of Steel</u>, American imports of British steel rails grew from only 20,506 tons in 1862, to 142,457 tons in 1864.

1876 view of the Bessemer steel plant of the Bethlehem Iron Company. Designed by John Fritz with assistance from Alexander Holley, it was the first Bessemer plant designed for integrated rail production and was the most efficient in America when it was completed in 1873. *From Harper's Weekly, March 25, 1876.*

The leading figure in the introduction of Bessemer steel production into America was Alexander Lyman Holley. During 1862-1863
Holley had gone to England on behalf of the New Jersey entrepreneur Edwin Stevens, who was constructing an ironclad warship.
Stevens sent Holley to Britain so he could bring back to America
the latest techniques in cannon and armor production. While in
England, Holley had an opportunity to make an extended visit to the
Bessemer steel plant near Sheffield. Recognizing the superior nature of the Bessemer process and the great American market for
steel rails, Holley returned to the United States determined to in-
troduce the manufacture of Bessemer steel. Supported by two
wealthy iron manufacturers from Troy, New York, he returned to
England and secured the American patent rights to Bessemer's invention. Soon afterwards in the United States, his backers, John F.
Griswold and John Flock Winslow, set him to work constructing an
experimental Bessemer plant at Troy. However, Holley and his backers were not the only Americans who were attempting to produce
Bessemer steel. On September 6, 1864, another group of entrepreneurs put into production the first American pneumatic steel plant
at Wyandotte, Michigan. Despite some initial success, this plant had
a short life and it exerted little influence on the subsequent development of the American steel industry.

Daniel J. Morrell, the principal partner in the Cambria Iron
Company, was also interested in steel production. During John
Fritz's tenure at Cambria, a Kentucky ironmaster, William Kelly, had
experimented with a pneumatic process of steel making. Although
great controversy exists as to the success of Kelly's experiment, he
was able to obtain a patent for his project in 1857. After securing
control of Kelly's patent, Morrell organized the Kelly Pneumatic
Process Company in 1863. This company in turn merged its efforts
with Holley's organization to form the Pneumatic Steel Association
in 1866. This reorganized enterprise was to become the catalyst for
the development of almost all of America's early steel plants.

Even before the Pneumatic Steel Association was organized,
Alexander Holley's pilot plant at Troy was successfully producing
Bessemer steel. John Fritz visited this facility in 1865. Despite
his admiration for Holley's achievement, he remained skeptical about
the sustained success of the Bessemer process in America. He also
remembered that Kelly's experiments at Cambria had not produced a
marketable product. Finally, he had become aware that the presence
of significant amounts of phosphorous in an iron ore would render
it unsuitable for use in a Bessemer converter. Since almost all of
the iron ores available to the Bethlehem Iron Company contained
what he thought were unsuitably high levels of phosphorous, he saw
little point in investing in a steel-making facility.

John Fritz's reluctance to build a Bessemer steel plant was not shared by Robert H. Sayre. Under his direction, the Lehigh Valley Railroad had imported a batch of British steel rails in 1865. These rails proved to be almost four times as durable as conventional wrought iron rails. Convinced that the Lehigh Valley Railroad needed a domestic source of steel rails, Sayre committed the Bethlehem Iron Company to steel production and made formal arrangements with the Pneumatic Steel Association to obtain use of its patent rights. Sayre was able to convince Fritz that Bethlehem must build a Bessemer plant. Fritz was also persuaded by the recently acquired knowledge that the introduction of spiegeleisen (low grade ferro manganese) into the charge of a Bessemer furnace would produce a steel suitable for rails.

In order to develop Bethlehem's steel-making facilities, John Fritz secured for the company a source of low phosphorous iron ores. He also assisted his brother George (who had remained at Cambria to become general superintendent), and Alexander Holley in designing the Bessemer plant and rolling mill that was being erected near Harrisburg by the newly formed Pennsylvania Steel Company. Begun in 1866, this enterprise was capitalized by the executives of the Pennsylvania Railroad, the Wilmington and Baltimore Railroad, and the Baldwin Locomotive Works. It was blown in for the first time in 1867 and its first steel ingots were rolled into rails at Cambria. Within a year, the Pennsylvania Steel Company had its own rolling mill in operation; its success further inspired John Fritz's own steel-making endeavors at Bethlehem.

Fritz began work on Bethlehem's Bessemer plant in 1868. Taking advantage of the experience he had gained while working with Alexander Holley and his brother George, John Fritz created a unique design for Bethlehem's steel-making facility. Applying his great skill as a mechanical innovator, Fritz was able to make it the first truly integrated steel plant in America. At the Bethlehem Iron Company, John Fritz combined Bessemer converters and rolling mills into a single production unit. Constructed in the shape of a double cruciform, this stone structure was 931 feet in length and 111 feet in width. Each of the four protruding transepts was 366 feet in length and 111 feet in width. The transepts provided the key to the plant's revolutionary nature, since each had a separate function. One transept housed four Bessemer converters, while its opposite number on the other side of the building housed the steel rail mill. The other two transepts contained machinery for making merchant bar stock. Each of the converters could produce eight tons of steel in a single blast. They were mounted in pairs and could be raised and lowered by hydraulic lifts. The engine that provided the blast for the converters was designed by Fritz to be particularly powerful and efficient. The steel rail train had a "three high" mill with rolls 28 inches in diameter.

The new plant was not completed until 1873, making it the tenth Bessemer steel plant ·to go into operation in the United States. During the last stages of its construction, John Fritz was ably assisted by Alexander Holley, who had become his close friend during the construction of Pennsylvania Steel Company's plant. Fritz benefited immeasurably from Holley's unrivaled knowledge and experience with the Bessemer process.

On October 4, 1873, the Bessemer converters of the Bethlehem Iron Company were first put into operation and on October 18 the first steel rails were rolled in the adjacent mill. Within a year, Bethlehem's new plant had established a national reputation both for its productivity and for the quality of its rails.

Soon after the successful completion of the Bessemer steel works at Bethlehem, the company also increased its pig iron production capacity. In 1874-1875 two new furnaces were built. These furnaces, No. 4 and No. 5, were 70 feet high and had diameters of 17 feet at the bosh, larger than almost all other American blast furnaces in use at that time. They were also blown by extremely powerful horizontal blowing engines.

Panoramic view of the works of the Bethlehem Iron Company showing both the anthracite iron and Bessemer steel production facilities. *From Frank Taylor, Autumn Leaves Upon the Lehigh, Philadelphia, Pa.* 1876.

Old Dick labored for almost 30 years at the Bethlehem Iron Company. He was 24 years old when this photo was taken in 1876. *John Fritz Collection, Hugh Moore Historical Park and Museums, Inc., Easton, Pa.*

Baldwin Locomotive Works photographs of the new Dick, a narrow-gauge locomotive that replaced old Dick in about 1880. *C. L. Bartholomew Collection.*

Since the Bethlehem Iron Company was still using anthracite as its primary blast furnace fuel, John Fritz hoped that these new furnaces would allow the company to remain competitive with the growing numbers of coke-fueled furnaces of western Pennsylvania. However, as he wrote in his Autobiography, this was not the case:

About this time coke began to be used in the furnaces in Western Pennsylvania and Eastern Ohio, and nearly double the amount of iron was made in the same sized furnaces that we could make with anthracite as a fuel. I thought that by building larger and higher furnaces and much more powerful blowing engines and by increasing the blast pressure from six to twelve pounds we could make as much iron in a given time with anthracite as they could with coke. Some of my Western friends came to Bethlehem to see our new furnaces and learn how they were working. They were so well satisfied with the result we had attained by high-pressure blast that they increased their blast pressure from about three and a half pounds to seven or eight, and we were again beaten about as badly as we had been before. We were the first, so far as I know, to use high-pressure blast.

As a result, the Bethlehem Iron Company began to increase its use of coke as a blast furnace fuel, although significant amounts of anthracite continued to be consumed by the blast furnaces until the early twentieth century. Growing demand for pig iron caused the Bethlehem Iron Company to build No. 6 Furnace in 1881. This furnace was 70 feet in height and 17½ feet in diameter at the bosh. Around the same time, the company acquired the North Penn Furnace in Bingen and designated it as No. 7, while simultaneously leasing and operating the Northampton Furnace at Shimersville. For a brief period in the 1890s, the company also leased and operated the Lucy Furnace near Dam No. 8 (Chain Dam) of the Lehigh Navigation near Glendon.

Although the Bethlehem Iron Company continued to prosper during the early 1880s, its share of the American railroad rail market began to decline due to the increasing competition from growing Pittsburgh-based firms such as the Carnegie Steel Company. Clearly, if the company was going to remain viable over the long term, a new product line had to be developed. Ironically, it was to be the newly perceived need for a modern American navy composed of steam-driven steel warships that would shape the course of the Bethlehem Iron Company's future development.

Although America had been a major naval power during the Civil War, the nation had allowed its navy to decline in the decades that followed. By 1881, the United States possessed a fleet that was composed largely of wooden-hulled steamers and sailing ships, and it was far inferior to the navies even of several Latin American nations. In 1882, the decision was made to rebuild the U.S. Navy, a step made necessary by America's growing world trade and national pride.

Fortunately for the United States, a revolution in naval technology enabled it to begin its rebuilding program on an almost equal footing with other nations. By 1880, several new developments had begun to make obsolete the existing squadrons of ironclads armed with wrought-iron muzzle-loading cannons. The perfection of the open hearth process made possible the production of steels sufficiently strong to withstand the forging process necessary for the creation of large caliber breech-loading cannon. Advances in metallurgy also made possible the development of face-hardened steel armor plate; this gave warships far superior protection with less thickness and weight than the conventional wrought-iron and steelcompound armor. The development of triple-expansion steam engines also was greatly aided by the development of open hearth steels. Triple expansion or "compound" engines greatly increased both the steaming power and cruising range of large warships. By choosing to develop warships when it did, the United States was able to take advantage of these new developments.

The U.S. government's decision in 1882 to rebuild its navy galvanized the Bethlehem Iron Company into a major expansion and technological upgrading of its facilities. Through its contacts with progressive naval officers, the most prominent of whom was Lieutenant William H. Jaques, secretary of the U.S. Navy's Gun Foundry Board, the management of the Bethlehem Iron Company learned that the navy would soon begin soliciting contracts for the guns, armor, and machinery needed to construct large steel warships.

To produce these items, a heavy forging plant would have to be constructed in the United States. With the support of other company officials, including Robert H. Sayre and several large stockholders such as Philadelphia industrialist Joseph Wharton, John Fritz convinced Bethlehem's board of directors to allow him to go to Europe to obtain the technology and patents rights that were needed to construct a heavy steel forging plant. He also received permission to build an open hearth steel plant, since Bessemer converters could not be regulated precisely enough to ensure good quality steel with every heat. Bethlehem's first battery of basic open hearth furnaces was fully operational by 1888.

When John Fritz returned from his European trip, he had learned enough about European heavy steel forging technology to enable the Bethlehem Iron Company to prepare successful bids in response to the U.S. Government's initial proposals for the new naval contracts. The Bethlehem Iron Company was the only American concern to bid on all of the contracts, and since its aggregate bid was the lowest it was awarded initial contracts totalling over $4,500,000.

The efforts of John Fritz and the other members of Bethlehem's management to make their company a major manufacturer of gun and armor forgings were greatly aided by Russell W. Davenport, who began as Fritz's assistant in 1888. A skilled metallurgist, he had acquired sound expertise in forging techniques while serving as superintendent of the Midvale Steel Company at Philadelphia. Midvale was a producer of cannon forgings, although it lacked Bethlehem's capacity.

Fritz, Sayre, and Davenport evolved a philosophy of management that made their entry into the production of guns and armor a success. When necessary, they were willing to pay a high price to import the most advanced methods and best machinery; they were then able to build on this foundation to produce a plant that was both technologically superior and more cost efficient than similar establishments of their more established European rivals. Using John Fritz's acknowledged genius for mechanical innovation, the Bethlehem Iron Company was able to build bigger and better forging devices than the British and French concerns that had originally licensed the needed technology to them. Thus, within five years of securing the rights from Sir Joseph Whitworth and Company to build heavy forging presses and the rights to build steam hammers from Schneider's, Bethlehem had surpassed both of these firms in the size and efficiency of these devices.

The specifications of Bethlehem's great steam hammer and forging press are particularly noteworthy since these machines owed much to John Fritz's genius for mechanical design. Manufactured completely at the Bethlehem plant, the steam hammer was mounted in a separate building, and rested on a solid foundation. Although its basic technology had been imported from Schneider's great Le Creusot Works, the Bethlehem hammer differed radically, due to John Fritz's mechanical innovations, from its French counterpart. An undated document from the Bethlehem Steel Company's collection at the Hugh Moore Historical Park and Museums, Inc., contains a detailed description of this massive machine:

> It rises to a height of 90 feet from the floor line. The housing proper are each composed of two parts, the lower ones weighing 11 tons each, the upper ones 48 tons each. These are bolted together and surmounted by an entablature of 61 tons carrying a 76 inch cylinder 24 feet high. The housings are clamped to base plates, each 10 feet by 8 feet and weighing 56 tons giving a 42 foot longitudinal width of frame and a working floor with inside housings of 22 feet. An 11 inch steel piston rod, 40 feet long, operates the

enormous top, which is composed of three parts, two forming a ram and a third the die. The hammer is single-acting (steam lifting only), the total weight of falling parts, length of stroke and gravity governing the work done. The anvil foundations consist of piles driven to bed rock or gravel, with timber frames, steel slabs and 22 iron blocks carefully machined and filled forming a metal mass of 1800 tons arranged in the form of a frustum or pyramid. To secure an even floor for working, the spaces between the frame and anvil foundations are enclosed with cribbing leaving exposed only the anvil block. The special valve gears designed at Bethlehem have worked most satisfactorily, the operator easily controlling the motions with one hand. The hammer is served by four heating furnaces, conveniently placed and by four gigantic cranes, each of 150 tons capacity, having longitudinal transverse, vertical and turning motions by which every required position and movement of the forgings can be easily controlled. In describing this hammer as one of 125 tons, it is meant that the weight of the top (including die) piston and rod is 125 tons, which falling a distance of 16½ feet (full stroke) without top steam produces the full power of the hammer.

Begun in 1889, the Bethlehem hammer was completed on June 3, 1891. It forged the armor plate for many of America's early steel warships and it was considered to be a mechanical wonder of the age. However, when a more efficient forging device was developed, John Fritz had no compunction about idling his expensive new hammer in 1893, and by 1901 it was scrapped. The new device was the hydraulic forging press.

In many ways, the great hydraulic forging press that Fritz designed and constructed for the Bethlehem Iron Company was even more impressive and useful than the massive steam hammer. Capable of exerting fourteen thousand tons of force, this press enabled its operators to have a much finer control over the forging process. It was particularly useful for the production of hollow-cored forgings. Each of its two hydraulic cylinders was 50 inches in diameter, and the entire press was powered by a three-cylinder, 15,000 horsepower steam engine.

By 1892 the Bethlehem Iron Company possessed the finest steel forging plant in the world, capable of producing armor plate and cannon of almost any size. It also produced engine forgings for the American ocean liners SS St. Louis and SS St. Paul, and the field rings for the generators of the new Niagara Falls hydro-electric power plant. Its forging capacity was graphically demonstrated when the company produced the axle for the famed Ferris Wheel, the

Close-up of the forging of what may be a field ring for the Niagra Falls hydro-electric generating plant. Bethlehem's 14,000-ton-force hydraulic press was extremely versatile and probably the most powerful open-die forging device in the country. 1894-1895. *Bethlehem Steel Corporation Collection, Hugh Moore Historical Park and Museums, Inc., Easton, Pa.*

Standard-gauge saddle-tank switch engine at the Bethlehem Iron Company in 1893, with its crew. Locomotives like this were used to move standard-gauge railroad cars around the plant. *John Fritz Collection, Hugh Moore Historical Park and Museums, Inc., Easton, Pa.*

Bethlehem Iron Company, as recorded by noted photographer William Rau in 1899. At that time the plant covered an area of 175 acres on the south bank of the Lehigh River in South Bethlehem. Facilities included blast furnaces, puddling mills, Bessemer steel converters, rolling mills, open hearth furnaces, steam-hammer and hydraulic-press forge shops, machine shops, tempering and treating departments. *William Rau Collection, Hugh Moore Historical Park and Museums, Inc., Easton, Pa.*

centerpiece of the 1892–1893 Chicago World's Fair. Weighing over 56 tons, this 45½-foot-long steel axle was the largest piece of forged steel known to have been made up to that date. It was the key component of the Ferris Wheel, which was 246 feet in height and took almost 20 minutes to complete a single revolution.

The products displayed by the Bethlehem Iron Company became one of the most visited exhibits at the fair. The full-size model of its great steam hammer and its large cannons outshone even the monster guns of the famed Krupp Company of Germany. Bethlehem had truly arrived as a full-fledged member of the arms and armor cartel. This new prominence was highlighted when Robert H. Sayre, in his capacity as general manager of the Bethlehem Iron Company, took his place in the presidential stand as America's new steel warships joined participants from the other world sea powers in an International Naval Review in New York Harbor. Designed as a part of the World's Fair festivities, this review showcased Bethlehem's products and won for the Company further prestige among the world's defense establishments. However, it should be noted that due to delays in the completion of Bethlehem's armor mill, the U.S. government, not wishing to be dependent on a single source, convinced the Carnegie Steel Company to build an armor plate mill at its homestead plant near Pittsburgh. This mill was completed in 1892.

By the time John Fritz retired as general superintendent in 1892, the Bethlehem Iron Company had completed the armor and cannon for America's first modern steel battleships, the USS Texas and the USS Maine. Work had also been finished on the cannon for the USS Oregon, a warship that would soon win worldwide fame. Completed in record time, the guns and machinery forgings for the USS Oregon served as Fritz's valedictory achievement as general superintendent.

Although John Fritz retired from active management of the Bethlehem Iron Company in 1892, the plant and management system that he had developed both continued to grow in size and importance. A year before Fritz's retirement, an artillery expert from the British Army, Lieutenant Colonel W. Hope, visited the Bethlehem plant and stated "I consider the Bethlehem Gun Plant to be superior to any gun plant in the world."

This tradition of excellence that had been built by Fritz was carried on by Robert H. Sayre and Russell W. Davenport. They were aided by Robert P. Linderman, who became president of the Bethlehem Iron Company in 1890. A grandson of Lehigh Valley Railroad financier Asa Packer and son-in-law to Robert H. Sayre, Robert P. Linderman proved to be an able financial officer whose activities contributed much to the Bethlehem Iron Company's continued success.

Pouring an armor plate ingot in 1892 at the No. 2 open hearth shop of the Bethlehem Iron Company. *John Fritz Collection, Hugh Moore Historical Park and Museums, Inc., Easton, Pa.*

Armor plate ingot being removed from a heating oven before being taken to the 14,000-ton forging press, 1894. *John Fritz Collection, Hugh Moore Historical Park and Museums, Inc., Easton, Pa.*

Three-cylinder 12,000 horsepower steam engine that provided the power for the hydraulic pumps of the 14,000-ton-force forging press designed by John Fritz. *John Fritz Collection, Hugh Moore Historical Park and Museums, Inc., Easton, Pa.*

1892 view of the 12,000 horsepower steam engine showing the hydraulic pump-driving mechanism. *John Fritz Collection, Hugh Moore Historical Park and Museums, Inc., Easton, Pa.*

Bethlehem Iron Company workers removing scale from a piece of armor plate, circa 1895. *Bethlehem Steel Corporation Collection, Hugh Moore Historical Park and Museums, Inc., Easton, Pa.*

The armor-plate finishing shop of the Bethlehem Iron Company in 1895. Equipment consisted of large saws, planers, and portable drill presses and grinders. Different groups of armor, assembled in the positions they would occupy on a vessel, were inspected in this shop before shipment. *John Fritz Collection, Hugh Moore Historical Park and Museums, Inc., Easton, Pa.*

During the last years of the nineteenth century, the products of the Bethlehem Iron Company played a crucial role in the development of the United States as a world power. Ships such as the Maine, Texas, Oregon, Iowa, New York, Brooklyn, and Olympia were equipped with Bethlehem-forged machinery, ordnance, and in some cases armor when they destroyed two Spanish squadrons at the battles of Manila Bay and Santiago. These victories brought the Spanish American War to a speedy conclusion and gained for the United States overseas territories and new standing as a world power. The Bethlehem Iron Company's contribution to victory was acknowledged when Sayre stood on the reviewing platform with President McKinley as the U.S. Navy passed in line during the victory review at the end of the war.

During the last years of the nineteenth century, the company made other notable technological and managerial advances. Between the years 1899 and 1901, Frederick W. Taylor was employed at the Bethlehem works where he made many of the time and motion studies that would become the core of his widely adopted principles of scientific management. He also worked with Munsell White to develop modern high-speed tool steels.

In 1899, the Bethlehem Iron Company was reorganized as the Bethlehem Steel Company. Robert H. Sayre and other longtime managers had retired several years earlier. In 1901, the Bethlehem Steel Company was purchased by Charles M. Schwab. At the time of Schwab's purchase, the Company's works stretched over 1½ miles along the Lehigh River and it employed over 6,000 men. It was quite profitable, never paying less than an 8 percent annual dividend since 1885.

Initially, Schwab merged the Bethlehem Steel Company into the abortive U.S. Shipbuilding Company, which passed into receivership in 1903. As a result, Schwab resigned from his position as president of the United States Steel Corporation and reorganized his properties on a firmer financial basis, creating the present Bethlehem Steel Corporation in December 1904. A massive building program was begun which lasted for over a decade. This program included the construction of the wide flange rolling mill designed by Henry Grey. The products of this mill were wide-flanged beams and other structural shapes that revolutionized the construction of high-rise buildings. By 1925 Schwab and his able young associate, Eugene Grace, greatly expanded the corporation by purchasing plants, such as Cambria Steel at Johnstown, Lackawanna Steel near Buffalo, New York, Steelton near Harrisburg, Pennsylvania, and Sparrows Point near Baltimore, Maryland. Bethlehem Steel thus became one of the largest steel makers in the world, and despite recent setbacks it remains a major force in the U.S. steel industry.

1902 view of 12-inch gun tube being forged by the Bethlehem Iron Company's 5,000-ton-force forging press. A hole was bored through the center of the ingot and a mandrel inserted. The gun tube is being forged around the mandrel. *John Fritz Collection, Hugh Moore Historical Park and Museums, Inc., Easton, Pa.*

Large gun forging, possibly 12-inch caliber, loaded on a large-capacity Lehigh Valley Railroad flat car for shipment from the Bethlehem Iron Company to the naval gun factory in Washington, D.C., or the Watervliet Arsenal near Albany, N.Y., circa 1902. The company often shipped finished guns to foreign governments, but standard American practice called for semi-finished pieces to be delivered to the navy or army. *Bethlehem Steel Corporation Collection, Hugh Moore Historical Park and Museums, Inc., Easton, Pa.*

This steam-operated forging hammer designed by John Fritz was the largest of its type ever constructed. It is seen here forging armor plate in 1891. *John Fritz Collection, Hugh Moore Historical Park and Museums, Inc., Easton, Pa.*

Bethlehem Iron Company's 7,000-ton force hydraulic forging press as it appeared in 1895. It was often used to straighten, bend, or give the final finish to armor plate. *John Fritz Collection, Hugh Moore Historical Park and Museums, Inc., Easton, Pa.*

1894 view of the 14,000-ton-force hydraulic forging press designed by John Fritz. This massive device could forge the largest sizes of guns and armor plate. It was served by two 200-ton capacity cranes with hydraulic lift and pneumatic travel.

John Fritz Collection, Hugh Moore Historical Park and Museums, Inc., Easton, Pa.

The 14,000-ton-force hydraulic forging press at Bethlehem forging a large piece of armor plate. The operator is standing on the platform on the right. In the background is the company's 125-ton steam hammer, which was idled by the development of the press. *Bethlehem Steel Corporation Collection, Hugh Moore Historical Park and Museums, Inc., Easton, Pa.*

An assembled 12-inch U.S. Army coastal defense gun mounted on a Buffington-Crozier "disappearing" carriage in 1894. When fired, the recoil forced the gun tube and the upper ends of the mounting arms of the carriage backwards and downward so they disappeared behind a heavy concrete wall. At the same time, the energy of the recoil raised a heavy lead counterweight that was housed in a deep well and attached to the opposite end of the mounting arms. After the gun was loaded a latch was tripped to release the counterweight, which raised the gun into firing position by its fall. Although the Bethlehem Iron Company usually supplied semi-finished gun-tube forgings to the U.S. Government, it delivered completely assembled disappearing guns. *John Fritz Collection, Hugh Moore Historical Park and Museums, Inc., Easton, Pa.*

Bethlehem Iron Company's fluid compression facilities in 1894. Molten steel used in the manufacture of guns and shafting was placed in a mould and subjected to hydraulic pressure until the ingot cooled.   *John Fritz Collection, Hugh Moore Historical Park and Museums, Inc., Easton, Pa.*

Chief Mechanic Jimmy Barron and his apprentice at a machine shop engine circa 1895.
Bethlehem Steel Corporation Collection, Hugh Moore Historical Park and Museums, Inc.
Easton, Pa.

Bethlehem Iron Company officials and visiting dignitaries celebrating John Fritz's 70th birthday on September 18, 1892, posing in front of the company's office building. Seated center front is Robert P. Linderman, company president, holding his grandfather Asa Packer's gold-headed cane. On his left is John Fritz, general superintendent; next left is Robert P. Sayre, general manager and Linderman's father-in-law; next left is Russell W. Davenport, assistant general superintendent and chief metallurgist; next left is E.P. Wilbur, president of the Lehigh Valley Railroad, who was a relative of Linderman and a close business associate of Robert Sayre. Thomas Edison is seated in the front, sixth from right. J.P. Morgan, the Wall Street investor who would later organize the U.S. Steel Corporation, is standing fourth from left in the fifth row. *John Fritz Collection, Hugh Moore Historical Park and Museums, Inc., Easton, Pa.*

Japanese government officials visited the Bethlehem Iron Company in 1902 to view the forging facilities and to negotiate the proposed sale of guns and armor to the Japanese navy. *Bethlehem Steel Corporation Collection, Hugh Moore Historical Park and Museums, Inc., Easton, Pa.*

1909 view of the Grey Mill of the Bethlehem Steel Corporation. This steam-driven machine made possible the economical production of rolled wide-flanged beams and columns that were lighter and stronger than conventional riveted "I" beams and made possible the construction of higher buildings and longer bridges. The original Grey Mill remained in operation until April, 1988. *Bethlehem Steel Corporation Collection, Hugh Moore Historical Park and Museums, Inc., Easton, Pa.*

Workers at the Bethlehem Steel Corporation standing on a completed main turret for the battleship U.S.S. Pennsylvania, designed to carry three 14-inch guns; the maximum thickness of its armor was 18½ inches. The Pennsylvania and its sister, the U.S.S. Arizona, carried four such turrets. 1914. *Bethlehem Steel Corporation Collection, Hugh Moore Historical Park and Museums, Inc., Easton, Pa.*

Number 3 High House at the Bethlehem plant in 1920. This 1887 facility housed a vertical heating furnace, an oil tempering well, and a high-capacity hoist. After being heated, gun tubes were lowered into the well for tempering. *Bethlehem Steel Corporation Collection, Hugh Moore Historical Park and Museums, Inc., Easton, Pa.*

206

Charles M. Schwab (1862-1939) transformed the Bethlehem Steel Company into the modern Bethlehem Steel Corporation. The protege of Andrew Carnegie, he became president of the Carnegie Steel Company in 1897. In 1900 he played a key role in making that company the core of the newly organized United States Steel Corporation. In 1901 Schwab became the first president of U.S. Steel, but due to disagreements with other managers and a need to devote his full energies to his other financial interests, he resigned in 1903. In 1901 Schwab had purchased control of the Bethlehem Steel Company; in 1904 he made it the basis for the modern Bethlehem Steel Corporation which, under his leadership during the next decades, became the second largest steel maker in the United States. *Bethlehem Steel Corporation Collection, Hugh Moore Historical Park and Museums, Inc., Easton, Pa.*

Demolition of Furnace No. 2 of the Glendon Iron company. Circa 1900-1902. *Canal Museum-Hugh Moore Park Collection, Easton, Pa.*

Furnace No. 4 of the Glendon Iron Company before its demolition. *Canal Museum-Hugh Moore Park Collection, Easton, Pa.*

CHAPTER VII

THE DECLINE OF IRONMAKING IN THE LEHIGH VALLEY

The anthracite iron industry reached the peak of its importance in the nation's industrial development in the years during and immediately following the Civil War. After the panic of 1873 it underwent a gradual decline. Many reasons contributed to this decline, all of them related to geography and capital. After 1875, eastern Pennsylvania was no longer the best location to produce iron and most of the existing furnaces were too undercapitalized to modernize, a prerequisite to survival in an increasingly competitive environment.

So long as anthracite coal was the most viable mineral fuel for iron production the Lehigh Valley was ideally situated. The canal builders who promoted the industry's development saw their dreams realized, and they prospered. The iron furnaces provided a huge new market for their coal, and canal traffic increased beyond their expectations. The ironmakers' use of New Jersey magnetic ores was a bonus. As the industry developed, canal boats that delivered coal to the New York market--boats that in earlier years had often returned empty--began making profitable westbound voyages carrying Morris County ores to the Lehigh Valley.

By the mid 1850s, however, the limitations of the canal system began to curtail the industry's growth. As more and larger furnaces were built, their demand for raw materials increased. It became increasingly difficult, and uneconomical, to lay in sufficient supplies of raw materials to keep the furnaces operating during the winter months when the canals were frozen over.

The answer to this problem was the building of the railroads. As early as 1854, the construction of the Lehigh Valley Iron Company's furnace at Coplay and the Thomas Iron Company's works at Hokendauqua were undertaken with rail shipments in mind. They were built along the proposed route of the Lehigh Valley Railroad, not along the Lehigh Canal. According to Samuel Thomas, there was considerable speculation as to which would be ready first, the Lehigh Valley Railroad or No. 1 furnace. As the furnace was completed on June 3, 1855, and the railroad was not officially opened until September 25, 1855, the first shipments of coal were delivered by the Lehigh Coal and Navigation Company to a dock across the slackwater pool behind the Hokendauqua dam.

For many years the railroads and the iron companies enjoyed a highly profitable symbiotic relationship, the railroads carrying the raw materials to the furnaces and consuming as much as 70 percent of the iron industry's product. By the 1870s, however, this relationship began to turn sour. The railroads, like the iron companies, sustained huge losses during the depression that followed the panic of 1873. In their effort to regain profitability, the anthracite coal carriers started to cooperate on setting their rates. This cooperation was eventually to result in one of the most brazen adventures ever undertaken by private companies to achieve monopolistic power. The reorganization of the anthracite coal carriers, led by the Philadelphia and Reading Railroad, is described very charitably by Randolph L. Kulp in Railroads in the Lehigh River Valley:

In a spectacular maneuver planned to control the entire anthracite coal industry's production and its transportation to markets as well as complete control of bituminous coal movements through eastern and northeastern sections of the United States, the Philadelphia and Reading Railroad Company entered into a series of contracts and leases with various railroads and anthracite and bituminous coal companies. The first lease became effective on December 1, 1891.

The huge monopoly included most of the anthracite coal companies: Lehigh Valley Railroad Company; The Central Railroad Company of New Jersey; Buffalo, Rochester and Pittsburgh Railroad; New York Central Railroad; Poughkeepsie Bridge Company; Central New England Railroad; and from May 1, 1892, until July 31, 1893, under temporary lease from receivers, Pennsylvania, Poughkeepsie and Boston Railroad. Philadelphia and Reading Railroad Company's passenger trains entered Hartford, Connecticut, on February 3, 1892. The unwieldy combine entered receivership on February 20, 1893, and financial and legal experts required several years of work to untangle the maze of leases and contracts.

Despite this plan's failure, the small merchant pig producers were at the railroads' mercy and suffered accordingly.

The superiority of coke as a blast furnace fuel was described earlier and many local ironmakers started to mix coke with anthracite as early as the 1870s. However, the coke was produced in ovens hundreds of miles from the eastern furnaces and delivered by the same carriers who had driven up the delivered price of anthracite. Some companies, like the Bethlehem Iron Company, that had close ties to the railroads may also have enjoyed more favorable rates than the small merchant pig producers.

In addition to the competition from the modern efficient furnaces that were erected in the Pittsburgh District during the 1870s, the local industry suffered from overexpansion resulting from the iron boom during the Civil War. The huge profits made during the war and the rapid expansion of the railroads in the post-war era led many "town fathers" to believe that a blast furnace was vital to the economic well-being of their communities. Often furnaces were built with locally subscribed funds and a lessee was sought to operate the plant. Such furnaces were often technologically deficient and many were operated for only a few years before being rebuilt or abandoned. The promoters of these plants generally expected a quick profit on their investment and were often reluctant to subscribe the additional funds required to make the venture a success.

The panic of 1873 damaged but did not destroy the local industry, even though many of the smaller operators were forced to file for bankruptcy. Most were reorganized with the bankers taking control. The bankers in turn were unwilling to make the expenditures required to modernize. Their judgment may have been sound, realizing the futility of trying to compete with the western furnaces.

The panic of 1893 was the deathknell for many of the local plants. In the depression that followed many were blown out for the last time. The plight of these local producers was vividly described by B.F. Fackenthal, Jr., president of the Thomas Iron Company, in his report to the company's stockholders drafted on October 19, 1897:

Few of our stockholders realize the bitter life or death struggle The Thomas Iron Co. is in to-day. When The Thomas Iron Co. started this plant in 1856 it was the pride of America and constantly referred to as a model by the best English and French authorities. Pig iron was high and The Thomas Iron Co. were the leaders in making foundry pig iron. Our Pig went to Pittsburg, to the North and to the south. In 1867 and 1868 Furnaces sprung up like mushrooms around the Lehigh Valley cutting into our market and lowering prices.

In 1870 furnaces were built on the Hudson, also at Troy, Utica, Syracuse, Scranton, Buffalo, all through the Shenango and Mahoning Valleys, Virginia and Maryland. The Pittsburg district put up Furnaces making double the old product. This cordon of furnaces told seriously on our market as they commenced to ship pig iron East.

In 1880, Pittsburg put up furnaces making 1800 tons, doubling the amount of 1870 in the same size Furnace, by using Fire Brick Stoves and more powerful Blowers. The Furnaces were built heavier and stronger. The rich Lake Superior ores were then beginning to force their way in the

Pittsburg district. Since 1890 larger and richer bodies of ore have been found in Lake Superior district and some of the larger Furnaces have increased their output each to 3500 tons per week in use of this rich ore. Take one firm, Carnegies. Formerly they bought greater part of their iron of the Furnaces around Pittsburg, to-day they make all their own pig, and the outlying Furnaces of Pittsburg send their iron East to knock down our prices and take away our customers . . . No better proof of the ruined condition of the pig iron business is needed than to see the number of Furnaces idle all though the country, many of them in the Receivers hands.

Because it was one of the better managed of the local merchant iron producers, the Thomas Iron Company, like the Empire Steel & Iron Company, not only survived this crisis but went on to enjoy the prosperity of the first decade of this century as well as that brought on by the great demand for iron during World War I. After the war, however, gloom again set in as prices fell. This situation was exacerbated by the importation of European iron, carried as ships' ballast and delivered to east coast ports where it was sold at prices lower than the production costs of locally produced iron. As the business outlook deteriorated the steel producers sold their excess pig iron on the merchant market, driving prices even lower. A few merchant furnaces were operated sporadically during the 1920s, but by the decade's end only the Bethlehem Steel Company had an operating blast furnace in the Lehigh Valley.

Engine house of Crane Iron Company before its demolition. Circa 1935. The furnaces have already been torn down. *Pennsylvania Canal Society Collection, Canal Museum, Easton, Pa.*

Lock Ridge furnace in 1930 after the Butz family had salvaged most of the materials that were easily removed. Later the elevators and even the masonry stock houses were dismantled. *Courtesy American Iron and Steel Institute.*

BIBLIOGRAPHY

Agreements Between the Lehigh Coal and Navigation Company and the Easton Power Company and Report on the Glendon Level. Easton, Pa., 1901.

Alderfer, E. Gordon, Northampton Heritage: The Story of an American County. Easton, Pa.: Northampton County Historical and Genealogical Society, 1953.

Anderson, Elaine, The Central Railroad of New Jersey's First 100 Years, A Historical Survey. Easton, Pa.: Center for Canal History and Technology, 1984.

Archer, Robert, The History of the Lehigh Valley Railroad. Berkley, California: Howell-North, 1977.

Bartholomew, Ann and Craig L. Bartholomew, A History of Lower Macungie Township, Lehigh County, Pennsylvania. East Texas, Pa.: Lower Macungie Township Bicentennial Committee, 1976.

Bartholomew, Craig L., "Anthracite Iron," Proceedings of the Canal History and Technology Symposium, Vol. III. Easton, Pa.: Center for Canal History and Technology, 1984.

Bartholomew, Craig L., "Anthracite Iron Making and Industrial Growth in the Lehigh Valley," Proceedings of the Lehigh County Historical Society, Vol. 32, 1978.

Bartholomew, Craig L., "William M. Weaver, Superintendent of the Macungie Furnace," Canal History and Technology Proceedings, Vol. V. Easton, Pa.: Center for Canal History and Technology, 1986.

Beers, D.G., Atlas of Northampton County, Pennsylvania. Philadelphia, Pa.: A. Pomeroy and Co., 1874.

Beers, F.W., County Atlas of Warren County, New Jersey. New York, N.Y.: F.W. Beers Company, 1874.

Berg, H.A., Alabama Blast Furnaces. Woodward, Alabama: Woodward Iron Company, 1940.

Bertland, Dennis B., Early Architecture of Warren County. Harmony, N.J.: Harmony Press, 1976.

Bertland, Dennis B., Shippen Manor Historic Structures Report. Princeton, N.J.: Heritage Studies, Inc. 1985.

"The Bethlehem Hammer," The Iron Age. July 13, 1893.

Binder, Frederick M., Coal Age Empire. Harrisburg, Pa.: Pennsylvania Historical and Museum Commission, 1974.

Bining, Arthur C., Pennsylvania Iron Manufacture in the Eighteenth Century. Harrisburg, Pa.: Pennsylvania Historical and Museum Commission, 1973.

Birkinbine, John, "Comparison of Blast Furnace Records" (contains David Thomas's discussion of fine dirt problems at Lock Ridge),

Transactions of the American Institute of Mining Engineers, Vol. XV, 1887.

Bloom, Kenneth and Marion Wolbers, *Allentown, Pa.: A Pictorial History*. Allentown, Pa.: Allentown Economic Development Corporation, 1984.

Board of Manager Minute Books of Lehigh Coal and Navigation Company 1825-1840 (microfilm copies at Hugh Moore Historical Park and Museums, Inc., Easton, Pa.)

Borough of Glendon 100th Anniversary, 1867-1967. Glendon, Pa.: Glendon Borough Centennial Committee, 1967.

Boyer, Charles S., *Early Forges and Furnaces in New Jersey*. Philadelphia, Pa.: University of Pennsylvania Press, 1931.

"The Bridge that Spanned the World." (Script for 1980 NOVA PBS TV Program)

Brown, Sharon, "The Cambria Iron Company of Johnstown, Pennsylvania," *Canal History and Technology Proceedings*, Vol. VII. Easton, Pa.: Center for Canal History and Technology, 1988.

Bryski, Anthony J., *The Lehigh Canal and Its Effects on the Economic Development of the Region Through Which It Passed 1818-1873*. (Unpublished Ph.D. Dissertation, N.Y.U. 1957)

Chard, Jack, *Making Iron and Steel the Historic Processes: 1700-1900*. Bugota, N.J.: Roebling Chapter S.I.A., 1986.

Coleman, Lyman, *Guidebook of the Lehigh Valley Railroad and its Several Branches and Connections*. Philadelphia, Pa.: J.B. Lippincott Co., 1872.

Cooling, Benjamin Franklin, *Gray Steel and Blue Water Navy: The Formative Years of America's Military-Industrial Complex, 1881-1917*. Hamden, Conn.: Archon Books, 1979.

Cooling, Benjamin Franklin, *Benjamin Franklin Tracy: Father of the Modern Fighting Navy*. Hamden, Conn.: Archon Books, 1973.

Condit, Uzal W., *The History of Easton, 1739-1900*. Easton, Pa.: George W. West, Publisher, 1953.

Cotter, Arundel, *The Story of Bethlehem Steel*. New York, N.Y.: Moody Magazine and Book Co., 1916.

Cotz, JoAnn, Herbert J. Githens, Brian H. Morrel and Edward S. Rutsch, *Historic Architectural/Industrial Archaeological Survey and Historic Planning Project for the Long Pond Ironworks Historic District, West Milford Township, Passaic County, N.J.* Newton, N.J.: Historic Conservation and Interpretation, Inc., 1982.

Crane, George, "Specification of a Patent for Smelting Iron with Anthracite Coal." Granted to George Crane. Sealed September 28, 1836, enrolled March 28, 1837, reprinted in the *Journal of the Franklin Institute*, Vol. 25. Philadelphia, Pa., 1838.

Crane, George, "On the Smelting of Iron with Anthracite Coal," Proceedings of the British Association for the Advancement of

Science. Mining Journal, reprinted in the Journal of the Franklin Institute, Vol. 25. Philadelphia, Pa., 1838.

Cummins, George W., History of Warren County. New York, N.Y.: Lewis Historical Publishing Co., 1911.

Davis, F.A. and H. L. Kockerperger, New Illustrated Atlas of Lehigh County, Pennsylvania. Reading, Pa.: Reading Publishing House, 1876.

Dickey, John M., Development and Feasibility Study of Oxford Furnace Historic Site, Warren County, New Jersey. Trenton, N.J.: Department of Conservation and Economic Development, Division of Park, Forestry and Recreation, 1970.

Directories of the American Iron and Steel Association, Philadelphia, Pa., 18741932.

Drake, J. Madison, (ed.), Warren County Historical Biographical and Industrial Review. Belvidere, N.J.: Belvidere Appollo, 1915.

Drinkhouse, W. Bruce, The Bethlehem Steel Corporation: A History from Origin to World War I. Easton, Pa. Northampton County Historical and Genealogical Society, 1964.

Edwards, Mark, A History of the Glendon Iron Works. (Unpublished Senior Dissertation, Lafayette College, 1974).

Ellis, F., History of Northampton County. Philadelphia, Pa.: Peter Fritts (Publisher), 1877.

Eschenbach, G.W., The Forks of the Delaware 1752–1900. Easton, Pa.: Eschenbach Printing House, 1900.

Fackenthal, B.F., The Durham Iron Works, Bucks County, Pa., Holicong, Pa.: Buckingham Friends Meeting House, 1932.

Fackenthal, B.F., "Early Iron Works, Chemists and Laboratories with Special Reference to Those at Durham Iron Works, 1870–1904", Bucks County Historical Society Papers, Vol. IX, 1942.

Fackenthal, B.F., Improving Navigation on the Delaware River with Some Account of Its Ferries, Bridges, Canals and Floods. Doylestown, Pa.: Bucks County Historical Society, 1927.

Fackenthal, B.F., Private Papers (Gathered together and arranged in 1939 at the Rare Book Room of Lucy Packer Lindermann Library, Lehigh University, Bethlehem, Pa.)

Fackenthal, B.F., The Thomas Iron Company, Fiftieth Anniversary Stockholders Report. New York, N.Y.: Post and Davis Co., 1904.

Firmstone, Frank, "Development in the Size and Shape of Blast Furnaces in the Lehigh Valley as Shown by Furnaces at the Glendon Iron Works," Transactions of the American Institute of Mining Engineers, Vol. XXXX. Published by American Institute of Mining Engineers, 1910.

Firmstone, William, "Sketch of Early Anthracite Furnaces," Transactions of the American Institute of Mining Engineers, Vol. III. Easton, Pa.: A.I.M.E., 1875.

Folsom, Burton W., Urban Capitalists. Baltimore, Maryland: Johns Hopkins University Press, 1981.

Foulke, C. Pardee, and William G. Foulke, Calvin Pardee: His Family and Enterprises, 1841-1923. Philadelphia, Pa.: The Pardee Co., 1979.

Friedman, Norman, U.S. Battleships: An Illustrated Design History. Annapolis, Md.: Naval Institute Press, 1985.

Fritts, Peter, History of Northampton County, Pennsylvania, 1752-1877. Philadelphia, Pa., 1877.

Fritz, John, The Autobiography of John Fritz. New York, N.Y.: John Wiley and Sons, 1912.

Fritz, John, Personal Papers of John Fritz (Hugh Moore Historical Park and Museums, Inc., Easton, Pa.)

John Fritz Pioneer in Iron and Steel. West Chester, Pa.: Chester County Historical Society, 1945.

Fritz, John, 1902 Testimonial Scrapbook (Hugh Moore Historical Park and Museums, Inc., Easton, Pa.)

Gemmel, Alfred, "Manuscripts Shed New Light on Lehigh County's First Furnace," Proceedings of the Lehigh County Historical Society, Vol. XVII, 1949.

General Catalog. Bethlehem Steel Company, 1904.

Gibbons, Tony, The Complete Encyclopedia of Battleships: A Technical Directory of Capital Ships from 1860 to the Present Day. New York, N.Y.: Cresent Books, 1983.

Hanson, Kenneth R., "Franklinite: Zinc, Iron and Manganese," Canal History and Technology Proceedings, Vol. VII. Easton, Pa.: Center for Canal History and Technology, 1988.

Hanson, Kenneth R., Port Oram Circa 1882: A New Jersey Iron Town. Scotch Plains, N.J.: Hanson Press, 1981.

Hanson, Kenneth R., "Richard and Mt. Hope: Two New Jersey Iron Mines," Canal History and Technology Proceedings, Vol. V. Easton, Pa.: Center for Canal History and Technology, 1986.

Harpster, Richard E., (ed.), Historic Sites of Warren County. Belvidere, N.J.: Warren County Freeholders, 1965.

Hazard, Erskine, "History of the Introduction of Anthracite Coal into Philadelphia," Memoirs of the Historical Society of Pennsylvania, Vol. II, 1827.

Heindel, Ned D., Iron, Armor and Adolescents: The History of Redington and the Carter Junior Republic. Easton, Pa.: Northampton County Historical and Genealogical Society, 1984.

Heller, William J., Historic Easton From the Window of a Trolley Car. Easton, Pa., 1911.

Heller, William J., History of Northampton County and the Grand Valley of the Lehigh. New York, N.Y., 1920.

Hellerich, Mahlon H., (ed.), Allentown, 1762-1987: A 225 Year history, Vols. I–II. Allentown, Pa.: Lehigh County Historical Society, 1987.

Henry, Matthew S., History of the Lehigh Valley. Easton, Pa.: Bixler and Corwin, 1860.

Hessen, Robert, Steel Titan: The Life of Charles M. Schwab. New York, N.Y.: Oxford University Press, 1975.

History of Armor Plate Manufacture for the U.S. Navy. Philadelphia, Pa.: American Iron and Steel Assoication, 1899.

History of Iron and Steel Making in the U.S. New York, N.Y.: A.I.M.M.E., 1961.

Hoffman, John N., Anthracite from the Lehigh Valley Region of Pennsylvania, 1820-1845. Washington, D.C.: Smithsonian Institution, 1968.

Holley, Alexander and Lenox Smith, "The Works of the Bethlehem Iron Company," Engineering (London), Vols. VII-XI, August 24–October 26, 1877.

Howell, Benjamin B., Esq., "Notes of the smelting of Iron by means of Anthracite, and of the origin of the hot blast in the manufac-ture of that metal," in a letter to the editor of the Journal of the Franklin Institute, Vol. 25. Philadelphia, Pa., 1838.

Johnson, Walter R., Notes on the Use of Anthracite in the Manufac-ture of Iron With Some Remarks on its Evaporative Powers. Boston, Mass. 1841.

Kalata, Barbara J., A Hundred years, A Hundred Miles. Morristown, N.J.: Morris County Historical Society, 1986.

Knaus, Oscar Penrose, History of Macungie. Macungie, Pa., 1932.

Krumgold, Joseph, (ed.), The Oxford Furnace. Belvidere, N.J.: Warren County Historical Society, 1975.

Kulp, Randolph L. (ed.), Railroads in the Lehigh Valley. Bethlehem, Pa. Lehigh Valley Chapter N.R.H.S., 1962.

Lambert, James F. and Henry J. Reinhard, A History of Catasauqua in Lehigh County, Pennsylvania. Allentown, Pa.: The Searle and Dressler Co., 1914.

Lee, James, The Morris Canal: A Pictorial History. Easton, Pa.: Delaware Press, 1988.

Lewis, Emanuel Raymond, Seacoast Fortifications of the United States: An Introductory History. Washington, D.C.: Smithsonian Institution Press, 1970.

Lewis, W. Davis, "The Early History of the Lackawanna Iron and Coal Company: A study in Technological Adaptation," Pennsylvania Magazine of History and Biography, Vol. XCVI, No. 4, October, 1972.

Lesley, J.P., The Iron Manufacturers Guide to the Furnaces, Forges and Rolling Mills of the United States. New York, N.Y.: John Wiley Publisher, 1859.

"Manufacture of Guns and Armor at the Bethlehem Steel Works," Scientific American. May, 1900.

Mathews, Alfred and Austin N. Hungerford, History of the Counties of Lehigh and Carbon in the Commonwealth of Pennsylvania. Philadelphia, Pa. 1884.

McHugh, Jeanne, Alexander Holley and the Makers of Steel. Baltimore, Md.: Johns Hopkins University Press, 1980.

Memorial Volume of Alexander Lyman Holley. New York, N.Y.: American Institute of Mining Engineers, 1884.

Metz, Lance E., John Fritz: His Role in the Development of the American Iron and Steel Industry and His Legacy to the Bethlehem Community. Easton, Pa.: Hugh Moore Historical Park and Museums, Inc., 1987.

Metz, Lance E., Robert H. Sayre Engineer, Entrepreneur and Humanist. Easton, Pa.: Hugh Moore Historical Park and Museums, Inc., 1985.

Miller, Benjamin LeRoy, Lehigh County, Pennsylvania, Geography and Geology. Harrisburg, Pa.: Pennsylvania Geological Survey, Fourth Series, Bulletin C-39, 1941.

Miller, Benjamin LeRoy, Donald McCoy Fraser, and Ralph LeRoy Miller, Northampton County, Pennsylvania. Harrisburg, Pa.: Pennsylvania Geological Survey, County Report 48, 1939.

Minute Book of Saucon Iron Company, Hellertown, Pa. 1871-1884. (Copy at Hugh Moore Historical Park and Museums, Inc., Easton, Pa.)

Morrell, Brian H., Historic Preservation Survey of the Morris Canal in Warren County, N.J. Belvidere, N.J.: Warren County Planning Board, 1987.

Morrison, Elling, From Know How to Nowhere: The Growth of American Technology. New York, N.Y.: Basic Books, 1974.

Mumford, John K., The Story of Bethlehem Steel 1914-1918 (Unpublished manuscript in Bethlehem Steel Corporation Collection, Hugh Moore Historical Park and Museums, Inc., Easton, Pa.)

Musicant, Ivan, U.S. Armored Cruisers: A Design and Operational History. Annapolis, Md.: Naval Institute Press, 1985.

Myers, Richmond E., Lehigh Valley the Unsuspected. Easton, Pa.: Northampton County Historical and Genealogical Society, 1972.

Nunn, J. Harold, The Story of Hackettstown, N.J.: 1754-1955. Hackettstown, N.J.: Hackettstown National Bank, 1954.

Ohl, Albert, Center Valley as I Found it 75 Years Ago and History of the Milfords, Lehigh County, Pennsylvania, Upper and Lower. 1732-1947.

Ohl, Albert, History of Upper Saucon Township, Lehigh County, Pennsylvania. 1732-1947.

Ordnance Material Catalog, Bethlehem Steel Company, 1904.

Percy, John, Metallurgy of Iron and Steel. London, England, 1864.

Porter, H.F.J., "The Radical Policy of Scrapping Costly Machinery," The Engineering Magazine, Vol. XX, No. 4, January, 1901.

The Properties and Plants of the Bethlehem Steel Corporation. Bethlehem, Pa.: Bethlehem Steel Corporation, 1925.

Recollections: In Celebration of 75 Years. Bethlehem, Pa.: Bethlehem Steel Corporation Public Affairs Department, 1979.

Records of Empire Steel and Iron Company 1899-1921 (manuscripts at Hugh Moore Historical Park and Museums, Inc. Easton, Pa.)

Richardson, Richard, Memoir of Josiah White, Philadelphia, Pa., 1873.

Roberts, Charles, History of Lehigh County, Vols. I-III. Allentown, Pa.: Lehigh Valley Publishing Co., 1914.

Roberts, Ed., "The Late David Thomas, Catasauqua, Pa.: Father of the Anthracite Iron Trade," The Cambrian, Vol. V, No. 4, April, 1885.

Roberts, Solomon W., "Obituary of the late George Crane, Esq., the founder of the Anthracite Iron Manufacture." Journal of the Franklin Institute, Vol. 41. Philadelphia, Pa., 1838.

Robson, Charles, editor, The Manufactories and Manufacturers of Pennsylvania. Philadelphia, Pa., 1875.

Rupp, I.D., History of Northampton, Lehigh, Monroe, Carbon and Schuylkill Counties. Harrisburg, Pa.: Hickok and Cantine, 1845.

Russell Wheeler Davenport (Memorial Volume). New York, N.Y.: G. P. Putnam, 1905.

Russo, A.L., An Historical Survey with Maps of the Industrial Sites Along the Lehigh Canal 1830-1880. (Unpublished Research Paper, Lafayette College, 1980).

Sayenga, Donald, "America's First Wire Rope Factory," Canal Currents, No. 56, Summer 1981.

Sayenga, Donald, "The Untryed Business, An Appreciation of White and Hazard," Proceedings of the Canal History and Technology Symposium, Vol. 2. Easton, Pa.: Center for Canal History and Technology, 1983.

Scrapbook of Lehigh Valley Railroad, 1870-1885.

Sellers, Coleman, "Hydraulic Forging Machines as Compared with the Action of the Steam Hammer," The Stevens Indicator, Vol. VI, No. 1, January, 1894.

67th Anniversary of the Founding of Glendon Borough. Glendon, Pa., 1934.

Snell, James P. History of Warren County, N.J. Philadelphia, Pa.: Everts and Peck, 1881.

Stapleton, Darwin H., The Transfer of Early Industrial Technologies to America. Philadelphia, Pa.: American Philosophical Society, 1987.

Stewart, Charles and Sayenga, Donald, (Ed.), "The Stewart Company," Canal History and Technology Proceedings, Vol. V. Easton, Pa.: Center for Canal History and Technology, 1986.

Swank, James M., History of the Manufacture of Iron in All Ages. Philadelphia, Pa.: The American Iron and Steel Association, 1892.

Swank, James M., Introduction to a History of Iron Making and Coal Mining in Pennsylvania. Philadelphia, Pa.: 1878.

Sweetser, Ralph, Blast Furnace Practice. New York, N.Y.: McGraw Hill, 1938.

Taylor, Frank H., Autumn Leaves Upon the Lehigh. Philadelphia, Pa.: James W. Nagale, 1978.

Temin, Peter, Iron and Steel in Nineteenth Century America: An Economic Inquiry. Cambridge, Mass.: M.I.T. Press, 1964.

Thomas, Samuel, "Reminiscences of the Early Iron Industry," Transactions of the American Institute of Mining Engineers, Vol. XXIX. New York: A.I.M.E., 1899.

Waltman, Charles, "The Influence of the Lehigh Canal on the Industrial and Urban Development of the Lehigh Valley," Proceedings of the Canal History and Technology Symposium, Vol. II. Easton, Pa.: Center for Canal History and Technology, 1986.

Warren, Kenneth, The American Steel Industry 1850-1970: A Geographical Interpretation. Oxford, England: Clarendon Press, 1973.

Weaver, Ethan Allen, The Forks of the Delaware. Easton, Pa., 1900.

Weaver, Valentine W., (Unpublished copies of business correspondence while Superintendent of the Millerstown Iron Company through February 28, 1878 and the Company's ledger listing all shipment of pig iron from October 2, 1874 through May 1879, original correspondence in possession of Craig L. Bartholomew, Emmaus, Pa. Microfilm copies in Collection of Hugh Moore Historical Park and Museums, Inc., Easton, ledger also at same location)

Wendt, Peter C., Boonton was an Iron Town. Boonton, N.J.: Boonton Historical Society, 1976.

White, Josiah, History Given by Himself, Philadelphia, Pa., 1904.

White, Trumbull, United States in the War with Spain. Chicago, Ill.: International Publishing Company, 1898.

Williams, David G., "Iron Mining in the Ironton Area, North Whitehall Township, Lehigh County, Pa." Proceedings of the Lehigh County Historical Society, Vol. 22, 1958.

Wynkoop, Ronald, Forks of the Delaware. Phillipsburg, N.J., 1975.

Wynkoop, Ronald, The Golden Years. Phillipsburg, N.J., 1970.

Wynkoop, Ronald, The Old Home Town. Phillipsburg, N.J., 1975.

Yates, W. Ross, Bethlehem of Pennsylvania: The Golden Years 1841–1920. Bethlehem, Pa.: The Bethlehem Book Committee, 1976.

Yates, W. Ross, "Discovery of the Process of Making Anthracite Iron," Pennsylvania Magazine of History and Biography, Vol. XCVIII, No. 2, April 1974.

Yates, W. Ross, Joseph Wharton, Quaker Industrialist. Bethlehem, Pa.: Lehigh University Press, 1987.

Yoder, C.P., Delaware Canal Journal. Bethlehem, Pa.: Canal Press, Inc., 1972.

Young, W.S., History of the Lehigh Coal and Navigation Company. Philadelphia, Pa., 1840.

CANAL HISTORY AND TECHNOLOGY
PROCEEDINGS

Volumes I, II, III, IV, V, VI and VII of the Proceedings are still available, while quantities last, from the Center for Canal History and Technology.

VOLUME I

"Railroad Versus Canal in the Southern Schuylkill Anthracite Coal Trade", by Spiro G. Patton.

"The Impact of the Lehigh Canal on the Moravian Settlement in Bethlehem", by Angelo Spinosa.

"Episodes from the Life of Canvass White, Pioneer American Civil Engineer", by Gerald Bastoni.

"An Examination of the Crellin Letters", by Lance E. Metz and Frank B. Davenport, Jr.

"Ellet and Roebling", by Donald Sayenga.

"The Pennsylvania Coal Company's Gravity Railroad", by Edward Steers.

VOLUME II

"Charles Ellet, Jr. and the Canal Versus Railroad Controversy", by Spiro G. Patton.

"According to His Own Lights: Benjamin Hughes, a Middle Level Manager in the Late Nineteenth Century", by Perry K. Blatz.

"Anthracite and Slackwater", by Terry K. Woods.

"Geographical Influences on the Development and Decline of the Union Canal", by Richard N. Pawling.

"The Influence of the Lehigh Canal on the Industrial and Urban Development of the Lehigh Valley", by Charles Waltman.

"The Untryed Business: An Appreciation of White and Hazard", by Donald Sayenga.

"The Delaware and Hudson Canal Company's Gravity Railroad", by Edward Steers.

VOLUME III

"The Illinois and Michigan Canal and Town Development in Northern Illinois", by J.K. Lamb.

"Anthracite Iron" by Craig L. Bartholomew.

"The Columbia and Philadelphia Railroad: A Railroad with an Identity Problem", by Albright Zimmerman.

"John Augustus Roebling and the Public Works of Pennsylvania", by Hubertis M. Cummings, edited by Donald Sayenga.

"The Delaware and Hudson Canal Company's Enlargement and the Roebling Connection", by Peter Osborne III.

"Roebling's Delaware Aqueduct During the 20th Century", by Harlan D. Unrau and Sandra Hauptman.

"The Restoration of Roebling's Delaware and Hudson Canal Aqueduct", by Sandra Speers.
"The Historical Significance of the Lehigh Coal and Navigation Company Engineering Records", by Charles L. Best.

VOLUME VII

"Franklinite: Zinc, Iron and Manganese", by Kenneth R. Hanson.
"The Cambria Iron Company of Johnstown, Pennsylvania", by Sharon Brown.
"The Life and Times of Pearl R. Nye: Balladeer, Historian, and Survivor of Ohio's Canal Era", by Terry Woods.
"The Ohio-Mississippi Waterway: Ellet's Dream and Army's Reality", by Donald Sayenga.
"The Middlesex Canal: Prototype for American Canal Building", by Thomas C. Proctor.
"The Pennsylvania Society for the Promotion of Internal Improvements: A Case Study in the Political Uses of Technological Knowledge, 1824-1826", by W. Bernard Carlson.
"Morris Foxall and the Eagle Works: A Pioneer Steam Engine Boring Cannon", by Charles Peterson.

Single copies are $11.00, plus $1.50 for postage and handling. A set containing Volumes I, II, III, IV, V, VI, and VII is $69.30 plus $4.00 for postage and handling. (Pa. residents add 6% sales tax). Send orders and make checks payable to the Center for Canal History and Technology, P.O. Box 877, Easton, Pa. 18044-0877.

BOOKS

The Central Railroad of New Jersey's First One Hundred Years: A Historical Survey, by Elaine Anderson, is the first major study of an important anthracite and commuter railroad. It is filled with photos, maps and timetables. It also includes information on the Company's Presidents, its marine division and anthracite coal mining subsidiary. It catches much of the color and many of the human-interest stories of America's "Big Little Railroad." - $14.00

Anthracite and Slackwater: The North Branch Canal 1828-1901 by F. Charles Petrillo is the definitive history of one of Pennsylvania's least known canals. It chronicles the engineering triumphs and failures of this waterway which linked the Wyoming Valley coal fields with both New York and the lower Susquehanna Valley. It is also the story of the men and women who worked on this waterway and the towns which grew up along it. - $16.25 (softcover) - $28.75 (hardcover)

The Delaware Canal Master Plan by Urban Research and Development and the staff of the Canal Museum - Hugh Moore Park provides a comprehensive overview of the problems and potential of Pennsylvania's Delaware Canal. A National Historic Landmark and the only towpath canal in America that is fully watered for almost its entire length, the Delaware Canal is a unique resource the history of which, along with its current conditions and recommendations for restoration, is fully documented in this publication. Containing many colored maps and historic and contemporary photos, The Delaware Canal Master Plan is a model for future canal research. – $11.20 (softcover)

The Death of a Great Company: Reflections on the Decline and Fall of the Lehigh Coal and Navigation Company by W. Julian Parton is the first major study of the demise of an anthracite coal company set within the general context of the decline of Pennsylvania's anthracite mining industry. Written by a former head of the company's coal mining operations, this volume is rich in the details of mining technology, and insights into corporate intrigue; as corporate raiders, intransigent unions and misguided executive decisions doomed America's oldest and proudest coal mining and transportation corporation. The book also highlights the social history of Pennsylvania's Panther Valley during the the first half of the Twentieth Century. – $9.95 (softcover) – $19.95 (hardcover)

The Old Middlesex Canal by Mary Stetson Clark is the chronicle of America's first important canal which became the engineering prototype for all of the other American canals that followed. Linking the rapidly developing Merrimack Valley with the seaport of Boston, the Middlesex Canal did much to bring about the industrialization of Massachusetts. Fully illustrated, The Old Middlesex Canal also contains a guide to the remaining portions of this catalytic waterway. – $9.95 (softcover) – $19.95 (hardcover)

Orders should be accompanied by $1.50 for postage and handling for the first book and $.75 for each additional book. Pa. residents should add 6% sales tax. Send orders and make checks payable to Center for Canal History and Technology, P.O. Box 877, Easton, PA 18044-0877.

MEMBERSHIP

HUGH MOORE HISTORICAL PARK AND MUSEUMS is a non-profit corporation formed to support the operation of the *Center for Canal History and Technology,* as well as the *Canal Museum* and *Hugh Moore Park.* Our Purposes are:

Historical – to preserve the artifacts, documents, and infrastructures which tell the story of transportation and related industrial development during the Towpath Canal Era.

Educational – to increase public understanding and appreciation of the Towpath Canals and their contributions to the Industrial Revolution.

Recreational – to provide an unspoiled recreational area where individuals and groups can enjoy wholesome outdoor activities.

Each is worthy of public and private support. Members of HUGH MOORE HISTORICAL PARK AND MUSEUMS sustain the activities of these facilities through annual donations.

TO JOIN...

If you're not already a member, please take the time today to choose one of the membership categories below and send your check along with your name and address to: HMHP&M, P.O. Box 877, Easton, PA 18044-0877. Thank you!

MEMBERSHIP CATEGORIES

BUSINESS, FOUNDATION AND INDIVIDUAL

Benefactor/Superintendent	$5,000+
Patron/Weighmaster	$1,000
Sponsor/Captain	$500
Sustaining/Locktender	$100

INDIVIDUAL AND FAMILY

Supporting/Canaller	$50
Contributing/Boatman	$25
Associate/Mule Driver	$15
NON-PROFIT, AND INSTITUTIONAL ORGANIZATIONS	$30

Membership benefits include:
Complimentary Museum and Canal Boat Ride passes
Our quarterly newsletter
Discounts on purchases, including books, symposium registrations, and park facility rentals
Invitations to exhibit previews, programs and social events
Free access to archival collections for research